Everyman, I will go with thee,
and be thy guide

Ménie Muriel Dowie

GALLIA

'The youngest storks are content with being told:
"Cribbly-crabbly, plurry-murry." They consider
this capital; but the elder ones want a deeper meaning,
or at least something about the family.'
The Marsh-King's Daughter – Hans Andersen*

Edited by
HELEN SMALL
University of Bristol

EVERYMAN
J. M. DENT · LONDON
CHARLES E. TUTTLE
VERMONT

J. M. Dent
Orion Publishing Group
Orion House
5 Upper St Martin's Lane
London WC2 9EA
and
Charles E. Tuttle Co. Inc.
28 South Main Street
Rutland, Vermont 05701, USA

Typeset by CentraCet Limited, Cambridge
Printed in Great Britain by
The Guernsey Press Co. Ltd, Guernsey, C. I.

British Library Cataloguing-in-Publication Data
is available upon request

ISBN 0 460 87719 4

CONTENTS

NOTE ON THE AUTHOR AND EDITOR

MÉNIE MURIEL DOWIE was born in Liverpool, 15 July 1867, the second daughter of James Muir Dowie (a Liverpool merchant) and Annie Dowie, and a granddaughter of Robert Chambers (author of *Vestiges of Creation* and founder of *Chambers's Dictionary*). Ménie Dowie was educated in Liverpool, Stuttgart and France. Throughout her childhood, the family made frequent trips to the Highlands of Scotland, where she acquired a life-long love of fishing and shooting. At eighteen, she began a career as a reciter of poetry. She first made her mark as an author five years later, when she published *A Girl in the Karpathians* (1890), an account of her travels through Ruthenia the previous summer. Dowie had travelled alone on horseback, wearing knickerbockers, leggings, and a short skirt that could be detached for long-distance riding; she ate the vegetarian diet of the peasant families with whom she stayed, smoked cigarettes, bathed in the streams, and spent her twenty-third birthday brushing up on her revolver skills in case she met with a wild bear. Late-Victorian readers were fascinated, and Dowie quickly became a celebrity figure, lecturing to packed audiences, and appearing regularly in the society pages of journals and magazines.

In 1891, Dowie married the journalist and travel writer Henry Norman. Over the next eight years, she travelled extensively around Europe, Asia, and North Africa with him. In 1893, she edited a collection of essays entitled *Women Adventurers*. *Gallia*, her first novel, appeared in 1895. The 'sheer audacity' of its treatment of sexual relations caused a sensation, and made Dowie one of the most prominent 'new woman' novelists. Over the next two years she wrote occasional journalism, and contributed short stories to *The Yellow Book* and *Chambers's Journal*, collected with new work in the volume *Some Whims of Fate* (1896). Two further novels, *The Crook of the Bough* (1899) and *Love and His Mask* (1901) followed, and between 1901 and 1902 she wrote weekly articles on gardening and general country matters for *Country Life*, published in volume form as *Things about Our Neighbourhood* (1903).

Although Dowie lived to be seventy-seven, she seems to have published nothing after the age of thirty-five. Her effective withdrawal from the literary scene after 1903 was probably motivated in part by her very public divorce case in January of that year. Henry Norman divorced her on the grounds of her adultery with the mountain-climber and writer Edward Fitzgerald. Dowie married Fitzgerald later that year, but the scandal may have made polite publishers reluctant to associate with her. It is not known whether she continued to write pseudonymously. The details of her life over the next several years are sketchy. She travelled extensively around Europe, Asia, and the Middle East. When in England, most of her time was spent on her farm at Marsden Manor, near Chichester, where she quickly established a distinguished reputation as a breeder of cattle. She exhibited pedigree Red Poll at shows around England, and exported animals to Africa in the later 1920s. Dowie was widowed in 1931, and her only child, Sir Henry Nigel St Valery Norman, was killed in action in 1943. In 1941, Dowie had emigrated to America, partly on health grounds (she suffered badly from asthma) and partly because she believed England was going to lose the war. She died at Tucson, Arizona on 25 March 1945.

HELEN SMALL is Lecturer in English at the University of Bristol. She is the author of *Love's Madness: Medicine, the Novel, and Female Insanity, 1800–1865* (1996), and the co-editor of *The Practice and Representation of Reading in England* (1996).

CHRONOLOGY OF DOWIE'S LIFE

Year	Age	Life
1867		Born in Liverpool, 15 July
c. 1872–85	5–17	Educated in Liverpool, Stuttgart and France

CHRONOLOGY OF HER TIMES

Year	Literary Context	Historical Events
1867	Dickens visits America	Second Reform Act
1868	Wilkie Collins, *The Moonstone* Browning, *The Ring and the Book*	February: Disraeli's first Cabinet. December: Gladstone's first Cabinet
1869	Lecky, *History of European Morals* John Stuart Mill, *On the Subjection of Women*	Third of the Contagious Diseases Acts
1870	Death of Dickens	Forster's Education Act. Franco-Prussian War. Opening of Suez Canal
1871	Lewis Carroll, *Through the Looking Glass* Hardy, *Desperate Remedies*	Paris Commune
1872	George Eliot, *Middlemarch* Butler, *Erewhon*	Secret Ballot Act
1874	Hardy, *Far from the Madding Crowd*	Disraeli's second Cabinet
1876	Eliot, *Daniel Deronda* Meredith, *Beauchamp's Career*	Victoria becomes Empress of India. Invention of telephone. Bulgarian atrocities
1877	Ibsen, *Pillars of Society* Zola, *L'Assommoir*	Russo-Turkish War, 1877–8. Edison's phonograph
1878	Hardy, *The Return of the Native*	Earliest use of electricity. Congress of Berlin
1879	Ibsen, *A Doll's House* James, *Daisy Miller*	London telephone exchange
1880	Charlotte Young, *The Clever Woman of the Family* Deaths of George Eliot and Flaubert	Gladstone's second Cabinet. Invention of pedal and chain bicycle. Transvaal declares itself a republic
1881	Ibsen, *Ghosts* James, *The Portrait of a Lady*	

Year	Age	Life
1885	18	Begins a short but successful career as a reciter in England
1890	22	During the summer, travels alone to Ruthenia, and on through the Carpathian Mountains on horseback
	23	In October, an account of her travels is published in the *Fortnightly Review* under the title 'In Ruthenia'; lectures at Leeds in the Autumn
1891	23	Lectures to a packed auditorium in Liverpool on 15 February; *A Girl in the Karpathians* is published in May and sells out within a few days; four English editions appear within the year, plus four American editions and one German
	24	Marries Henry Norman, journalist and travel writer, on 28 August; after honeymooning in Scotland, she travels to Italy and the South of France, while he travels to Malaya

Year	Literary Context	Historical Events
1882	Leslie Stephen, *Dictionary of National Biography* (–1891)	Phoenix Park murders. F. Forest invents the combustion engine
1883	Nietzsche, *Thus Spake Zarathustra* Olive Schreiner, *The Story of an African Farm*	
1884	Moore, *A Mummer's Wife*	Third Reform Act
1885	Meredith, *Diana of the Crossways* Ryder Haggard, *King Solomon's Mines*	Fall of Khartoum. Salisbury's first Cabinet
1886	James, *The Bostonians* Stevenson, *Dr Jekyll and Mr Hyde*	Liberals split on Home Rule. February: Gladstone's third Cabinet. August: Salisbury's second Cabinet
1887	Conan Doyle, 'A Study in Scarlet' Hardy, *The Woodlanders* Strindberg, *The Father*	Victoria's Golden Jubilee
1888	Havelock Ellis, *Women and Marriage* Mrs Humphry Ward, *Robert Elsemere*	
1889	Stevenson, *The Master of Ballantrae*	London Dockers' Strike
1890	Gissing, *The Emancipated* 'Mark Rutherford', *Miriam's Schooling*	Parnell scandal. First 'tube' railway
1891	Gissing, *New Grub Street* Hardy, *Tess of the d'Urbervilles* Morris, *News from Nowhere* Wilde, *The Picture of Dorian Gray*	Free elementary education

Year	Age	Life
1892	24–5	Fifth edition of *A Girl in the Karpathians*; travels extensively in Egypt and the Sudan with Henry Norman; over the next few years, writes regularly for *The Daily Chronicle* and other periodicals
1893	25	January, begins a tour of the North of England, lecturing in Newcastle, Darlington, Liverpool and elsewhere on her Egyptian travels; edits and publishes a collection of autobiographical pieces entitled *Women Adventurers*
1895	27	'Wladislaw's Lament' appears in *The Yellow Book* in January; 'The Hint O' Hairst' in the February issue of *Chambers's Journal*; *Gallia* is published on 20 February by Methuen in London and J. P. Linnicott in Philadelphia; a second edition appears later in the year
	28	From September to December, travels through Eastern Europe with her husband; in November, has an interview with Madame Stambouloff in Sophia, and publishes an account of it in *The Daily Chronicle*
1896	28	Mrs Oliphant reviews *Gallia* in the January issue of *Blackwood's Magazine*; 'An Idyll in Millinery' published in *The Yellow Book* in July
	29	*Some Whims of Fate*, a collection of Dowie's short stories, is published in London and New York in October
1897	29	Second edition of *Some Whims of Fate*; her son, Henry Nigel St Valery Norman, is born on 21 May

Year	Literary Context	Historical Events
1892	Kipling, *Barrack-Room Ballads* Conan Doyle, *The Adventures of Sherlock Holmes*	Gladstone's fourth Cabinet. Panama scandal
1893	George Egerton, *Keynotes* Gissing, *The Odd Women* Sarah Grand, *The Heavenly Twins*	Foundation of Independent Labour Party
1894	Edward Carpenter, *Marriage in a Free Society* Emma Frances Brooke, *A Superfluous Woman* Mona Caird, *The Daughters of Danaus* Sydney Grundy, *The New Woman* Moore, *Esther Waters* First issue of *The Yellow Book*	Collapse of the three-decker novel
1895	Hardy, *Jude the Obscure* Conrad, *Almayer's Folley* Wells, *The Time Machine*	Trial of Oscar Wilde. Jameson raid. Salisbury's third Cabinet
1896	Wells, *The Wheels of Chance*	
1897	Conrad, *The Nigger of the Narcissus* Bram Stoker, *Dracula* *The Yellow Book* ceases	Queen Victoria's Diamond Jubilee. Tate Gallery opens

Year	Age	Life
1898	30–31	*The Crook of the Bough* published in London and New York
1899	31	September, travels to Russia with her husband and their close friend, the mountain climber and author, Edward Fitzgerald; returns with Fitzgerald to Brussels, and then England while Henry Norman continues to Central Asia; Norman learns of her adultery with Fitzgerald when he returns in December
1900	32	'In the Haunted Crimea' published in the *Contemporary Review* in July
	33	Campaigns on behalf of her husband in South Wolverhampton during the lead-up to the General Election at the end of September
1901	33	January, separates from Henry Norman; *Love and His Mask*, her last novel, is published
	34	1 December, publishes the first of a long series of unsigned articles in *Country Life*, entitled 'Things about Our Neighbourhood'
1902	34	24 February, Henry Norman petitions for divorce, on grounds of her adultery with Fitzgerald
	35	22 November, publishes the last of the 'Things about Our Neighbourhood' series
1903	35	Divorced from Henry Norman, 29 January; custody of their child is given to him; marries Edward Fitzgerald; *Things about Our Neighbourhood* published in volume form
1903–c. 1920	36–53	Travels extensively in Europe, Asia, India, Egypt

Year	Literary Context	Historical Events
1898	Havelock Ellis, *Women and Marriage* Shaw, *Plays Pleasant and Unpleasant*	Fashoda incident. Discovery of radium
1899	Wilde, *The Importance of Being Earnest* Elgar, *Enigma Variations*	Second Boer War starts
1900	Conrad, *Lord Jim* Wells, *Love and Mr Lewisham* Deaths of Wilde and Nietzsche	Relief of Ladysmith and Mafeking
1901	Kipling, *Kim*	Death of Queen Victoria. Accession of Edward VII
1902	James, *The Wings of the Dove* Conrad, *Youth* Butler, *The Way of All Flesh*	End of the Boer War. Balfour's Cabinet
1903	Shaw, *Man and Superman* Conrad, *Typhoon*	Emmeline Pankhurst founds the WSPU. First motorless flight in a powered, heavier-than-air machine
1904	Conrad, *Nostromo*	Anglo-French Agreement. Russo-Japanese War. Rutherford discovers radioactivity
1905	James, *The Golden Bowl*	Russia defeated by Japan. Campbell-Bannerman Prime Minister
1906	Galsworthy, *The Man of Property*	Liberal landslide victory at General Election
1907	Conrad, *The Secret Agent* Gosse, *Father and Son* Joyce, *Chamber Music*	

Year	Age	Life
1903–c. 1920	36–53	Travels extensively in Europe, Asia, India, Egypt

Year	Literary Context	Historical Events
1908	Grahame, *The Wind in the Willows* Bennett, *The Old Wives' Tale* Forster, *A Room with a View*	Herbert Asquith Prime Minister
1909	H. G. Wells, *Ann Veronica* Pound, *Personae*	Old Age Pensions introduced in Britain
1910	Forster, *Howards End*	Death of Edward VII; accession of George V; Tonypandy riots. First Post-Impressionist Exhibition
1911	Lawrence, *The White Peacock* Beerbohm, *Zuleika Dobson* Barrie, *Peter Pan* (volume form)	Scott and Amundsen race each other to the South Pole. Parliament Act limits the power of the Lords to veto legislation. Agadir crisis
1912	Conan Doyle, *The Lost World*	Sinking of the *Titanic*. Woodrow Wilson elected US President
1913	Frances Hodgson Burnett, *The Lost Prince* Lawrence, *Sons and Lovers* Katherine Mansfield, *In a German Pension*	Panama Canal opened. Hunger strikes by suffragettes
1914	Joyce, *Dubliners* Wyndham Lewis, *Blast* Compton Mackenzie, *Sinister Street*	Assassination of Archduke Franz Ferdinand of Austria in Sarajevo; Britain declares war on Germany and Austria-Hungary
1915	Buchan, *The Thirty-Nine Steps* Ford Madox Ford, *The Good Soldier* Conrad, *Victory* Woolf, *The Voyage Out* Lawrence, *The Rainbow*	Gallipoli. Sinking of the *Lusitania*. Asquith leads coalition government
1916	Joyce, *A Portrait of the Artist as a Young Man* Death of Henry James Shaw, *Pygmalion*	Battles of Jutland and the Somme. Easter Rising in Dublin. Lloyd George leads coalition government. Battle of Jutland
1917	Eliot, *Prufrock and Other Observations*	Russian Revolution; Lenin and the Bolsheviks assume power. US enters the war. British victory at Passchendaele

Year	Age	Life
c. 1920	53	With Edward Fitzgerald, purchases Marsden Manor, near Cirencester, and takes up farming; by the mid-1920s she has established a considerable reputation as a breeder of pedigree Red Poll cattle
1924	57	Visits Italy
1927	60	Travelling in Europe, Africa and Egypt; exports cattle to Mombasa
1928	61	c. August, leaves Edward Fitzgerald; travels to Austria, and Cairo

Year	Literary Context	Historical Events
1918	Wyndham Lewis, *Tarr* Lytton Strachey, *Eminent Victorians*	Collapse of the Central powers. End of the war. Russian Civil War; Tsar Nicholas II assassinated. First trans-Atlantic return flight
1919	Maughan, *The Moon and Sixpence* Woolf, *The Voyage Out*	Treaty of Versailles. Socialist uprising in Berlin crushed. Rosa Luxemburg murdered; Nancy Astor becomes the first woman MP
1920	Lawrence, *Women in Love* Edith Wharton, *The Age of Innocence* Djuna Barnes, *Nightwood*	League of Nations founded
1921	Lytton Strachey, *Queen Victoria* *Athenaeum* ceases publication	Red Army wins Russian Civil War. Einstein wins Nobel Prize for Physics
1922	Eliot, *The Waste Land* Joyce, *Ulysses*	Mussolini takes power in Italy. Stalin becomes Soviet leader
1923	Yeats wins Nobel Prize for Literature	Failure of Hitler's attempted coup in Munich. Stanley Baldwin Prime Minister
1924	P. C. Wren, *Beau Geste* Forster, *A Passage to India* Mann, *The Magic Mountain*	Death of Lenin. Ramsay MacDonald Prime Minister in minority Labour government
1925	P. G. Wodehouse, *Carry On Jeeves* Scott Fitzgerald, *The Great Gatsby*	Conservative government, Baldwin Prime Minister
1926	Dorothy L. Sayers, *Clouds of Witness* Kafka, *The Castle* Hemingway, *The Sun Also Rises*	General Strike
1927	Rosamond Lehmann, *Dusty Answer*	Lindbergh flies from New York to Paris
1928	Death of Hardy Lawrence, *Lady Chatterley's Lover* banned	Women over 21 years of age win the right to vote

Year	Age	Life
1929	61	January, serious illness in Cairo (possibly malaria); recovers, and travels to Venice and then Vienna to recuperate
	62	October 1929, officially separates from Fitzgerald; living in 38 Green St, Mayfair
1931	63	Edward Fitzgerald dies at Marsden Manor on 2 January
1932–41	64	Living at Shepherd's Crown, South of Winchester, but making regular trips abroad
1941	73	Emigrates to Arizona on health grounds
1943	75	Her son is killed in action on 19 May

Year	Literary Context	Historical Events
1929	Woolf, *A Room of One's Own* Graves, *Goodbye to All That* Hemingway, *A Farewell to Arms*	Wall Street crash
1930	Death of Lawrence Auden, *Poems*	
1931	Woolf, *The Waves*	Ramsay MacDonald Prime Minister of National Government
1932	Huxley, *Brave New World*	F. D. Roosevelt US President
1933	Dorothy L. Sayers, *Murder Must Advertise*	Hitler Chancellor in Germany Roosevelt inaugurates The New Deal
1934	Graves, *I, Claudius*	
1935	MacNeice, *Poems*	Baldwin Prime Minister
1936	Huxley, *Eyeless in Gaza* Auden, *Look! Stranger*	Spanish Civil War begins Edward VIII accedes in January, abdicates in December
1937	Woolf, *The Years* David Jones, *In Parenthesis*	Chamberlain Prime Minister
1938	Greene, *Brighton Rock* Sartre, *La Nausée*	
1939	Joyce, *Finnegans Wake*	Germany, under Hitler, invades Poland. Britain and France declare war. Russia invades Poland and Finland
1940	Hemingway, *For Whom the Bell Tolls*	Germany invades Denmark and Norway; Churchill Prime Minister of Coalition Government
1941	Death of Woolf Woolf, *Between the Acts* Brecht, *Mother Courage* Death of Joyce	Germany invades Holland, Belgium, Russia; France capitulates in June. Japan attacks Pearl Harbour; US and Britain declare war on Japan
1942	Camus, *L'Étranger*	Dieppe raid. British attack at El Alamein
1943	Eliot, *Four Quartets* Somhairle MacGill-Eain, *Dàin do Eimhir agus Dáin Eile*	Allies invade Italy

Year	Age	Life
1945	77	Dies at Tucson, Arizona on 25 March

Year	Literary Context	Historical Events
1944	Anouilh, *Antigone*	D-Day landing in Normandy. Allies enter Paris in August
1945	Orwell, *Animal Farm* Waugh, *Brideshead Revisited*	VE Day, 8 May

INTRODUCTION

When *Gallia* was published in 1895, its reviewers were deeply divided. Few wanted to contest that this was a remarkable first novel from a twenty-seven year old writer – one which could fairly be said to have opened up new possibilities for fiction. Whether or not fiction *should* be interested in such possibilities was another matter. Dowie's strongest supporters believed that she had finally shown the way for novelists to write honestly about women: 'At last the likeness of the new woman has been caught and committed to paper with audacity, fidelity, and literary skill' enthused *The Queen* magazine.[1] But this was hardly a claim to recommend *Gallia* to every reader. The frankness Grant Allen brought to the subject of sex in *The Woman Who Did* (1895) threatened to pale into insignificance beside Dowie's handling of the theme. 'A lady has stepped in where even a Grant Allen has not dared to tread', warned *The Saturday Review*:

> there is no denying that Miss Ménie Muriel Dowie... has gone further in sheer audacity of treatment of the sexual relations and sexual feelings of men and women than any woman before. 'Gallia' is remarkable for extraordinary plainness of speech on subjects which it has been customary to touch lightly or to avoid, and the anatomy of emotion shows a coolness and daring, and the analysis of character an uncompromising thoroughness, for which the ordinary male reader finds himself unprepared.[2]

The Daily Telegraph was even less tolerant. Gallia was 'a monstrously eccentric heroine': an alarming confirmation of the current fascination with the decadent and the degenerate rather than with good, healthy, English normality.[3] Margaret Oliphant, reviewing *Gallia* together with *The Woman Who Did* and

Thomas Hardy's *Jude the Obscure* in early 1896 similarly deplored the emergence of an 'Anti-Marriage League' in recent fiction.[4] There were worse fates for a first novel than to be denounced in such company.

Given the stir that *Gallia* created on its first appearance and the resurgence of interest in New Woman fiction over the last few years, it seems odd that there should have been so little interest in Ménie Muriel Dowie to date. *Gallia* is the first of her novels to be reprinted since publication, and she has attracted very little critical attention beyond brief references in a handful of recent works.[5] Part of the reason is undoubtedly that so few details have been available about her life. Indeed, one prominent critic of New Woman fiction has seen Dowie's fate as typical of that suffered by many radical novelists of the late nineteenth century: 'what happened to Ella Hepworth Dixon, Ménie Muriel Dowie, Dorothy Leighton, and George Paston? If these writers published nothing after their New Woman novels, were their retreats from the literary marketplace "honourable"?' Such questions often 'cannot be answered, because the primary documents – the correspondence, diaries, journals, and other private papers that might enable us to answer them – either have not been saved or could not be located'.[6]

In fact, it is possible to retrieve a great deal of information about Ménie Muriel Dowie's life not only from her own writings, but from periodicals of the time, and from personal recollections of people who knew her. She was every bit as defiant of convention as the heroine of her first novel, and before looking at *Gallia* in more detail, it is worth examining the ways in which her experiences and her attitudes set the terms for the novel's reception in 1895. More tentatively, Dowie's life after *Gallia* suggests a number of reasons why, by the time she died in 1945, her reputation as one of the most provocative writers of the turn of the century should have been almost entirely forgotten.

Dowie's Life[7]

Ménie Muriel Dowie was born in Liverpool on 15 July 1867. She was the second daughter of a Liverpool merchant, James Muir Dowie, and his wife Annie Dowie, and a granddaughter of the Edinburgh publisher Robert Chambers (author of *Vestiges of Creation* and founder of the Chambers dictionaries and encyclopaedias). Among her cousins she could count Rudolph Lehmann of *Punch*, the composer Mme. Liza Lehmann and Sir Joseph Priestley. James Muir Dowie's commercial interests involved the family in extensive travel and his daughter's education was consequently divided between Liverpool, Stuttgart and France. The Scottish connection nevertheless remained important. The Dowies regularly hired shoots in the Highlands, where Ménie developed a life-long passion for hunting and fishing.

At eighteen Dowie began a career as a reciter of poetry – probably in Liverpool. A photograph from this time shows her as a strikingly beautiful woman, slim, with waist-length blonde hair. In 1890, she abandoned the stage for more adventurous pursuits. During the summer of that year she travelled across France and Germany to Ruthenia. From there, she journeyed on horseback through the Carpathian mountains, alone except for a peasant guide. Her travelling costume was improvised and eminently practical: knickerbockers, and a short skirt detachable on long rides. Dowie ate the vegetarian diet of the families with whom she stayed, bathed in the streams, smoked constantly, and contended fearlessly with the persistent fleas. A large part of her twenty-third birthday she spent brushing up on her revolver skills in case she met with a wild bear (to her disappointment, the bears stayed away).

Back in England in early autumn, Dowie quickly set about putting her experiences into print. An essay about her travels was published in *The Fortnightly Review* late in 1890, preliminary to the appearance of a book the following year. While *A Girl in the Karpathians* was in progress, Dowie gave at least two public lectures: one in Leeds in the autumn, and one in

Liverpool in January. The Liverpool event was attended by a reporter for *The Woman's Herald*:

> Last Sunday Miss Ménie Muriel Dowie lectured for the Liverpool Sunday Society in the Rotunda Lecture Hall, on 'A Forgotten Country'. The hall was crowded, and a large number of persons were unable to gain admission.
>
> After giving a sketch of the history of Poland in the form of a fairy tale, she gave an account of her visit there last summer. She has a charming manner and a very pleasant delivery, so that her audience were kept entranced during the whole of the lecture, which lasted over an hour.... The part of the lecture of most interst to women was that where Miss Dowie described the dress she wore during her stay in the mountains. It consisted of a shirt, knickerbockers, short skirt, and jacket, and she said that the comfort of such a costume is more than one can tell; she never felt so well in her life as she did while wearing it. Her belief is that women will never rise to what they ought to be, until the present mode of dress is changed, for it cramps both mind and body.[8]

This was stirring feminist stuff, good grist to the newspaper's ongoing campaign in support of 'rational dress',[9] but Dowie was clearly not in the business of antagonising the male members of her audience. The male reviewer of *A Girl in the Karpathians* for *The Queen* magazine was florid in his praises: 'Miss Dowie, in the warmer weather, deserted the "blue basin" of her chamber, and made her toilet *al fresco*, "straying over the ragged river-bed barefoot to the weir".... Miss Dowie completes a fair picture of herself as the nymph of the waters and the flower of the morn.'[10] It seems more than likely that, far from resenting the element of patronage in such reports, Dowie encouraged them. Certainly the image of her as roguishly feminine, a robustly healthy rebuke to the neurotic type of new woman, recurs time and again in contemporary notices.

A Girl in the Karpathians was a roaring success. It rapidly went through five English and four American editions, plus one German printing. Dowie was a celebrity. When she married the respected journalist and travel-writer Henry Norman on 28 August, the event was avidly recorded in society magazines despite the fact that it was not a 'fashionable marriage' at all in the accepted sense, but a modest ceremony in the registry office at St George's Hanover Square, with Henry Norman's Malaysian servant and Dowie's maid as the only witnesses. The honeymoon, spent fishing and hunting in Scotland, offered more in the way of journalistic copy: 'The figure of Mrs Norman issuing to the chase in a smart Tauntz knickerbocker suit, with a cigarette between her lips, and a salmon rod in her hand electrifies the sober Scot, who has never seen anything so charmingly unconventional before.'[11]

Dowie was just twenty-four years old, and had written only one book, but the reading public was eager for more and her career was followed with interest in the literary papers and society magazines of the day. Almost as soon as the honeymoon was over, she was reported to be off to Italy and the South of France while her husband travelled to Malaya to oversee progress at his gold mines[12] (Norman had obtained a concession from the King of Siam in the late 1880s, allowing him to mine gold in Malaya). In 1892, the Normans travelled together to Egypt and the Sudan, where the usual tourist trecks not surprisingly failed to attract Dowie. On her return to England, she gave a series of lectures around the North of England, including Newcastle, Darlington and Liverpool on her itinerary.[13] Her title was 'Through Egypt with Ennui' and 'Ennui' was not, as The Daily Chronicle noted wittily, the name of her courier, but an expression of her feelings about 'the average tourist's life in Egypt'. Scorning the beaten track, she and Norman had travelled out to the far outposts of the Sudan, where they were able to witness the aftermath of recent fighting and take numerous photographs, with which Dowie illustrated her talks. All this was good background for the appearance of her next book, a collection of biographical studies of women cross-dressers, travellers, explorers and fighters, edited by Dowie and racily entitled Women Adventurers.

Dowie's first published work of fiction appeared in The Yellow Book in January 1895. Like Gallia, 'Wladislaw's Lament' is set in Paris, and it anticipates the novel's detached take on familiar decadent themes: bohemianism, the art world, prostitution. It tells the story of a struggling Polish artist, asked to pose for the figure of Christ. Wladislaw turns up at the painter's studio at the appointed time, and finds, in the dressing room, a costume which he assumes he is intended to wear. He puts on the white, ascetic robes, struck by their look and feeling of authenticity: Christ himself might have worn such a garment. Wladislaw draws aside the curtain of the studio and walks forward into a scene of decadent abandon: the artist has forgotten the appointment, and is in the midst of a lavish and debauched entertainment. At the sight of Wladislaw the party freezes, then hysteria breaks out. They are convinced that this is Christ himself, and the Day of Judgment has come. Only when one prostitute, braver or more depraved than the rest, leaps on Wladislaw, kisses him, and forces him to drink, does their terror begin to ebb away. 'There is perhaps a moral in Wladislaw's story', the narrator concludes, but 'if so, I have had no thought to write it.' The gestures and, in some respects, the action are recognisably of a type with other *Yellow Book* tales, but the style is sparer, relying for its effects not on witty epigram or on richness of verbal surface, but on the startling force of its central idea. A second story followed quickly: a romantic tragedy set in Scotland, entitled 'The Hint O'Hairst'. It was published in February 1895 in *Chambers's Journal*, and both story and venue suggested a rather nostalgic return to origins on Dowie's part.[14] A year later, another tale appeared in *The Yellow Book*, and at the end of 1896 all three were collected with two new pieces in the volume *Some Whims of Fate*.

Gallia was published on 20 February 1895, and Methuen were not slow to capitalise on the established celebrity of their new author. Wherever *Gallia* was advertised or reviewed, it was billed as 'by the author of *A Girl in the Karpathians*' or, more commonly, 'by the Girl in the Karpathians'. Miss Dowie's work since her first book had 'not satisfied the perhaps excessive expectations of her first critics', according to *The Saturday Review*, but *Gallia* was the book they had been waiting for: 'she has been biding her time, accumulating material, and developing a criticism of life'.[15]

Successful though the book was as first novels go, its reception by the general reading public was perhaps not as enthusiastic as Dowie might have expected given the popularity of her first book. Sales were good enough to warrant a second edition later in the year, but no more than that. *The Woman Who Did*, a far less skilful novel in many respects, was nevertheless more conventionally 'sensational' and went through nineteen editions in 1895 alone, earning its author £1,000 a year until his death in 1899.[16] Late Victorian readers may have preferred the cheap melodrama of Allen's conclusion (his heroine commits suicide with prussic acid) to the subtleties of *Gallia*'s emotional dilemmas. Dowie herself was fully aware that, amidst all the noise created by 'the sex question' in the 1890s, original voices were easily lost. Gallia's reply when she is asked by her friends to commit her radical ideas on marriage and childbirth to paper suggests as much:

> Gallia shook her head briskly.
> 'One would only be grouped with all the other women who are said to be leading the "Sexual Revolt", and that would do the ideas harm, for no one would take them seriously.'
> 'But so much attention is paid to what women write now.'
> Gallia smiled drily . . .
> 'That's just it! What they say makes so much noise that nobody hears properly what it is. A woman who really feels these things shouldn't write about them now, until what they call the boom of women is over.'
> (pp. 115–16)

Soon after the publication of *Gallia*, Dowie was travelling again – this time accompanying her husband on an extensive tour of the Near East, including Germany, Hungary, Romania and Bulgaria. Henry Norman was now assistant editor of *The Daily Chronicle* and had been commissioned (or had commissioned himself) to write a series of articles on Eastern European politics. It is likely that Dowie contributed various pieces to his reports, but only one is definitely identifiable as by her hand. While visiting Sofia in November, she obtained an interview with Mme. Stambouloff, the widow of the Prime Minister of Bulgaria, brutally assassinated earlier that year. Dowie's account of her visit to the Stambouloff house caused a sensation among *The Daily Chronicle*'s readers.[17] She managed to combine a sense of the romance of the event (the pathos of the beautiful young widow) with a startling line in brutal realism. The interview took place in a study cluttered with memorabilia of the dead man, mostly official portraits, but also photographs of Stambouloff 'as he was laid out in his frock-coat':

> One eye-brow cut off; his lip gashed and swollen out of human semblance; his forehead and temples scarred in every direction; his empty cuffs – these had a peculiarly ghastly effect – and his dissevered hands and thumb affixed to a cloth and hung beside him.[18]

It was not the sort of stuff Victorian readers, even in the 1890s, were accustomed to finding in their daily paper.

Throughout the late 1890s and early 1900s, Dowie wrote regularly for *The Daily Chronicle* and other periodicals. Most of her articles were on women's issues, and were published anonymously. She attended occasional dinners for women writers in London (a signed menu indicates that she met Mona Caird at one such event), and she is known to have become acquainted with Thomas Hardy and Sir Henry Morton Stanley, about this time. Later, she came to know Rosamond Lehmann well. Lehmann, a distant relation, was fascinated by Dowie and portrayed her (not entirely flatteringly) in several novels. In 1901, Dowie began a series of articles about gardening and other country matters for *Country Life*.[19] She wrote only two more novels after *Gallia*: *The Crook of the Bough* (1898) and *Love and His Mask* (1901). The former she considered the best of the three. It tells the story of an unemancipated young woman (one of the new class of 'typewriter girl'), whose plainness and practicality earn her the attentions of a handsome Colonel, tired of more conventionally feminine women. Romance makes her light-headed, however, and she loses her lover when she meta-morphoses into exactly the kind of flirtatious female he has been trying to avoid. *Love and His Mask* is in many ways the more original book. Its heroine, Leslie, is a young, wealthy widow, who unburdens her mind to a male friend in a series of forthright letters, and who, though she keeps his friendship, finally marries another man. It bears more than a trace of the events in Dowie's own life over the previous two years – events which may well have lain behind her withdrawal from fiction-writing after 1903.

In 1899, Dowie, now the mother of a two-year-old boy, travelled with her husband to Russia. They were accompanied by their close friend, the celebrated mountain climber and author, Edward Fitzgerald. At Tiflis, Henry Norman discovered that he was obliged to continue on to Central Asia, and he left his wife and friend to travel back to England together *via* Brussels. Norman returned home in December, to find that his wife's manner towards him had changed. He had reason to believe she was in love with another man, but she denied it. Publicly, they remained close for at least a year longer. When he stood as the Liberal candidate for South Wolverhampton in September 1900, she was by his side, campaigning vigorously in support of his 'sound Liberal imperialism'.[20] Dowie's speeches were so popular that at least one reporter questioned whether the voters would be making a decision about the candidate or about his wife. Norman's Unionist opponent, William Oulton, ex-Lord Mayor of Liverpool, was hopelessly upstaged. He was so vexed at the unfairness of the contest that he started insisting that his wife accompany him onto the lecture platform – though he was unable to persuade her to open her mouth.[21] Henry Norman won handsomely.

The public view of the Normans' marriage as a close personal and political partnership was increasingly far from the reality, however. Sometime early in 1901, Norman discovered that his wife had been having an affair with Edward Fitzgerald since the end of their Russian trip. In February 1902 he filed for divorce. At the end of January 1903 the case came to court, uncontested. Norman was awarded a decree *nisi*, with costs, and custody of their child was given to him. Details of the case were published in *The Times* on 30 January for everyone to see. The occasions of Dowie's adultery were spelt out, and the gradual breakdown of the marriage painfully charted. For Norman, as a Member of Parliament and a well-known political journalist, it must have been deeply humiliating. For Dowie, it meant public disgrace and private misery. Her name was banned from Henry Norman's house, and she did not meet her son Nigel again until he was a student at Oxford in the late 1910s. While he was at school at Winchester, she went occasionally to watch him play sport, but was forbidden to make herself known. 'You cannot possibly know,' she wrote to Henry Norman's second wife in 1909, 'what the horror of being cut off from him has meant.'[22] It is not known whether she received a reply.

Dowie married Edward Fitzgerald in 1903, soon after her divorce from Henry Norman. Most of the following decade was spent abroad: in India, big-game hunting in the Himalayas, and in Asia, Europe and North Africa. Edward Fitzgerald had substantial private means, and some time around 1920 he purchased Marsden Manor, near Cirencester. There Ménie Fitzgerald, as she now called herself, took up farming, specialising in breeding Red Poll cattle. By the late 1920s she could claim to have established the finest pedigree herd in England. She exhibited at shows all over the country, and on at least one occasion (in 1927) she exported animals to Mombasa.

The Fitzgeralds' married life was clearly not easy. Edward Fitzgerald drank heavily (he started each day at eleven o'clock with a glass of champagne and a digestive biscuit, and continued tippling steadily). Dowie seems to have consoled herself with lovers, frequent trips abroad and, above all, with the running of Marsden Manor. By 1928, however, she had had as much as she was prepared to take of her husband and his dissolute friends. After a stormy scene, Dowie left Cirencester, and fled to Austria, then Egypt. In Cairo in January 1929, she became seriously ill. Her son flew out from London, fully expecting that he would find her dying. In fact, she recovered, and after a long recuperation in Venice and Vienna, she returned to England.

Concerted efforts by friends to persuade her to return to her husband were unavailing, and in October 1929, she took legal steps to separate her finances from his. Fitzgerald died on 2 January 1931, but any hopes Dowie might have had of moving back to Marsden Manor were rapidly squashed. When the estate was investigated, a vast proportion of Fitzgerald's fortune proved to have disappeared. An embezzlement case against his former secretary failed, and Marsden Manor had to be sold.

During the 1930s Dowie lived primarily at Shepherd's Crown, near Winchester, where she was able to see a great deal of her son and grandchildren. She continued to travel extensively. She enjoyed a drink, and she still chain-smoked, despite the fact that she suffered badly from asthma and was increasingly dependent on a vapouriser. By 1940, her health was so bad that she made the decision to move to Arizona where the air would be kinder to her lungs. She was influenced in no small part by a firm conviction that England was going to lose the war. Risking the considerable dangers of trans-Atlantic travel in wartime, she emigrated in early 1941, and purchased a plot of land in Tucson. When her grandson, Torquil Norman, joined her the following year, the new bungalow was completed. The walls were thick, designed to stand the weight of the second storey which would be needed to accommodate the rest of the family when the Germans won the war.

When Nigel Norman was killed in action, flying over France in 1943, Dowie was devastated. To many observers, she seemed to have lost her passion for living. She died at Tucson on 25th March 1945. *The Times* obituary, describing her as 'Mrs E. Fitzgerald: Author and Traveller', assumed that few of its readers would remember Ménie Muriel Dowie, and mourned her death as the breaking of 'an interesting link back to the world of the nineties.'

Gallia

A number of things are more easily understood about *Gallia* when details of the author's life are brought into play. The novel's intimate knowledge of Parisian life, its fluency with international politics, its 'insider' account of the Liberal aristocracy, become more readily explicable from a twenty-seven year old woman when it is known that she had travelled extensively since early childhood, and that she was married to one of the leading Liberal writers of the day. Even certain aspects of the novel's style – its preference for pithy dialogue rather than description, and its noticeable liking for metaphors drawn from hunting – take on a slightly different flavour in light of Dowie's own interests. But reading Ménie Muriel Dowie's life into *Gallia* is also problematic, and paradoxically more legitimate for being so, because this is a novel centrally concerned with the difficulties of making stories out of people's lives. Where Dowie's own history has most in common with *Gallia* is not in specific details, but in its sheer unpredictability: its suggestion of not one life story, but of several stories begun and not completed – deliberately abandoned, or reluctantly let go.

Gallia opens with what looks like a false start. At least one reviewer complained that the first five chapters were pretty well redundant. They are concerned not with Gallia but with the man she will eventually select as her ideal of healthy masculinity, Mark Gurdon. Gurdon wants to be a success in life. He intends to go far in the civil service – or, more accurately, he intends not to remain a mere underling at a desk in the Colonial Office. But when Gurdon seeks to ingratiate himself with a powerfully connected old lady by calling in on her grandson, in Paris, he is confronted by ample evidence that it is not so easy to shape one's own life. Robert Leighton, Oxford educated with Gurdon, and destined by birth and upbringing to lead the life of a gentleman, has forfeited the good opinion of most of his family by deciding instead to train as an artist. Two years ago, Gurdon and Leighton were almost indistinguishable as 'types' of the young English gentleman. Now, Gurdon still looks 'exactly as one would have expected' – the very model of a modern civil servant – but Leighton has lost all pretension to gentility: he wears his hair long, sports a weird bohemian beard, and filthy bohemian clothes, and lives openly with a French mistress.

Gurdon finds his encounter with the aging English model, Lemuel, if anything more disturbing. Lemuel, he discovers, was once, like himself, a junior member of the civil service. Now, he spends his working hours posing for painters, and the rest of the time drinking his earnings.

Gallia's story is taken up at the point where Gurdon makes the first decisive step in forging a career for himself. Their two stories continue to run side by side for the rest of the novel. But whereas Mark knows exactly what he must do if he is to 'go somewhere' in life (make himself discreetly indispensable to Her Majesty's government), Gallia's ability to control her future is far less certain. Like Gurdon, she has just completed a course of study at Oxford University (though as a freelance, she has not been able to take a degree). But what is the university-educated girl, wealthy enough not to have to work for a living, to do next? One of the hallmarks of Dowie's fiction is her tendency to begin writing 'after the event': that is, as though the most obviously compelling stories that might be told about her characters were already in the past, and not that interesting or significant after all. The 'Girton girl' and her Oxford equivalent were compelling subjects for fiction in the 1890s, but Dowie takes up her heroine's story after Oxford, at a curiously unpromising moment. Similarly, the fact that Gallia has been a fervent promoter of agricultural reforms in the past is produced as an amusing anecdote rather than a significant contribution to the development of the narrative.

When Gallia renews an acquaintance with Dark Essex, a decadent Fellow of Balliol College, Oxford, who treats her with cavalier disregard for the usual politenesses, romance seems to be one possibility. But Dowie has no interest in teasing out a conventional love story. She announces straightforwardly that Gallia *is* in love with Essex, but does not yet know it. By the end of the chapter, Gallia does know it, and knows also that she has been rejected. But her unhappiness at being told that the man she loves has no room for her in his life is far less acute than the painful conviction that she has behaved unseemingly. When Essex calls to return a book, she takes the opportunity to address him frankly. Having requested him to take a seat, she places a hand on his shoulders, and a firm finger under his chin, and obliges him to look at her while she informs him that she does indeed love him, and that, though she fully accepts his inability to return her feelings, she wants his forgiveness for the flagrant immodesty with which she 'sat there and said nothing' instead of openly stating her position. Initially thrown off balance, Essex soon rallies to his own defence. 'Don't you think the world is still a little too raw for your very advanced treatment of it?' he asks.

Such forensic interest in the 'anatomy of emotion' perplexed many of the book's first readers and it still has the ability to surprise. Time and again, Dowie takes the familiar materials of romantic fiction – the declaration of love, the proposal scene, even the deathbed scene – and turns their assumptions inside out. Her writing is at its best in rigorously analytic scenes like the one between Gallia and Essex. Gallia scorns hypocrisy where her feelings about other people are concerned. Her determination to deal openly and honestly with the question of sexual attraction is reminiscent of the attitude of radical contemporary thinkers like the sexologist Havelock Ellis. Gallia too wants to know how emotion works, how far it is bound and distorted by convention, how far the bearer of emotion may be compromised by it and how far they might hope to be liberated.

Dowie's men and women talk constantly. By far the larger part of the book is devoted to conversations rather than to startling events or lengthy descriptions. In this respect, Dowie's closest fictional antecedent may well be Mrs Gaskell, whose novels are similarly centred on debate about social ethics. Whether Dowie's works could be said to advocate social improvement as Mrs Gaskell's ultimately do is another question. *Gallia*'s central and most radical idea – the one which most upset early readers – is its heroine's growing conviction that the 'real advance' in society will be the careful selection of fathers and mothers on comparable criteria to those currently employed in the hiring of servants:

such a scheme would be eminently rational. The outcome of the present health movement must lead that way. People will see the folly of curing all sorts of ailments that should not have been created, and then they will start at the right end, they will make better people. How can we wonder that only one person in ten is handsome and well made, when you reflect that they were most likely haps of hazard, that they were unintended, the offspring of people quite unfitted to have children at all?

(p. 113)

With Dowie's later success as a cattle-breeder in mind, it would be easy to miss the note of irony that accompanies her treatment of Gallia throughout the novel. But Gallia's views are rarely unambiguously endorsed by the narrator. Here, she is never quite delivered from the cheap but persuasive suspicion, voiced by her friend Gertrude, that all this devotion to the future health of society is just a result of being jilted.

When Gallia refers to 'the present health movement' she clearly means the late nineteenth-century interest in eugenics. Behind her advocacy of selective breeding programmes to ensure the future strength of society can be heard the voice of Francis Galton, the most influential British advocate of scientifically-informed government intervention in childbirth ('practical Darwinism', as he saw it). Behind Galton's eugenics lay a profound anxiety about the degeneration of the European race: a fear which makes itself felt in Gallia's revulsion against Dark Essex's small, refined, feminine hands and her immediate approval of Mark Gurdon's finely proportioned physique. At the same time, Gallia's avowed concern about the future of society sits uncomfortably with her unrepentant – indeed ruthless – individualism. Dowie informs the reader early on that Gallia's first great intellectual passion was for the social ethics of John Stuart Mill and Herbert Spencer. She has evidently taken to heart Spencer's defence of individual freedom against state intervention, though quite what she makes of Spencer's views on the inferiority of the female mind[23] and how she reconciles his beliefs with those of Mill remain unclear.

Gallia makes a serious intervention in some of the most

pressing debates of its day – sexology, degeneration, eugenics – but it is also a witty book, and one which, even in the heat of the argument, never allows its heroine to escape too long from the gentle tug of authorial irony. Gallia's desire to find fulfilment by becoming the mother of healthy children takes the novel to a complex and emotionally uncertain conclusion. Her belief that heredity is the key to the future, and her desire to fashion a valuable life for herself in the light of that belief, evidently hold the potential for tragedy, but tragedy is not this novel's dominant mode. The title-page epigraph, taken from Hans Christian Andersen's *The Marsh-King's Daughter*, is one reminder that this book is as much social comedy as it is sociology, and as riddling as it is serious. Andersen's tale tells of a fairy princess abducted by a sinister marsh king; and of a child born out of the marsh in the cup of a lily flower, who possesses by day the beautiful form of her mother but the cruel heart of her father, by night the grotesque frog form inherited from the marsh king but the gentle heart of the princess. Like many fairy tales it is about cruelty and about the destructiveness of selfish desire, but its harshness is controlled and to a large extent defused by the comic role of the storks who pass this story down from generation to generation. Dowie's novel is similarly concerned with large and serious questions about the degree to which individual lives are shaped by the forces of heredity, but, like Andersen's fable, its seriousness is repeatedly inflected by a comic awareness that human lives are more prone to metamorphosis than Gallia herself would want to allow.

HELEN SMALL

References

1. Douglas Sladen, ' "Ga-lia" – The Real New Woman', *The Queen*, 9 March 1895, p. 432. Other positive reviews included W. A., 'A Book of the Time', *The Daily Chronicle*, 27 February 1895, p. 3.
2. [Anon.], 'Gallia', *The Saturday Review*, 23 March 1895, pp. 383–4 (p. 383).
3. Unsigned review, *The Daily Telegraph*, 8 March 1895, p. 6.

4. M.O.W.O. [Margaret Oliphant], 'The Anti-Marriage League', *Blackwood's Edinburgh Magazine*, January 1896, pp. 135-49.

5. Gail Cunningham's short discussion of *Gallia* in *The New Woman and the Victorian Novel* (London: The Macmillan Press Ltd, 1978), 73-6, is an unusual exception.

6. Ann Ardis, *New Women, New Novels: Feminism and Early Modernism* (New Brunswick: Rutgers University Press, 1990), p. 166.

7. The following short biography draws on private correspondence and personal reminiscences (see Acknowledgements). Published materials have been referenced where relevant.

8. C.W.P., 'Miss Dowie in Liverpool', *The Woman's Herald*, 21 February 1891, p. 274.

9. *The Woman's Herald* advertised itself as 'The Only Paper Written, Conducted and Published by Women'. It devoted itself to women's issues, encouraging its correspondents to air their views on the rights and wrongs of smoking, marriage, higher education, women's role in politics and other pressing questions of the day.

10. *The Queen*, 30 May 1891, p. 845.

11. *The Woman's Herald*, 12 September 1891, p. 742.

12. *The Queen*, 24 October 1891, p. 683.

13. I am grateful to Patrick French for drawing my attention to this material.

14. 'Dowie', as she noted in a footnote to the story's epigraph, was Scottish for 'sad', 'It's dowie in the hint o' hairst' meaning 'It's sad at the end of harvest'. 'The Hint O'Hairst', *Some Whims of Fate* (London: John Lane, The Bodley Head, 1897), p. 51.

15. [Anon.], 'Gallia', p. 383.

16. See Cunningham, *The New Woman and the Victorian Novel*, p. 63.

17. A. T. Camden Pratt (ed.), *People of the Period: Being a Collection of the Biographies of Upwards of a Thousand Living Celebrities*, 2 vols. (London: Neville Beeman Ltd, 1897), I, 336.

18. [Henry Norman and Ménie Muriel Dowie], 'Round the Near East: xv. Stambouloff v. Stoiloff. / Where is Vengeance? / A Talk with a Brave Woman', *The Daily Chronicle*, 18 November 1895, p. 5.

19. Collected as *Things about Our Neighbourhood* (1903).

20. Description of Henry Norman's political stance in *The Daily Chronicle*, 26 September 1900, p. 6.

21. I am grateful to Patrick French for this information.

22. Quotation courtesy of Patrick French.
23. For discussion, see Janet Oppenheim, '*Shattered Nerves*': *Doctors, Patients and Depression in Victorian England* (New York: Oxford University Press, 1991), pp. 182–3.

NOTE ON THE TEXT

The text of *Gallia* used for this Everyman edition is the 1895 Methuen first edition, with some silent alteration of punctuation, according to Everyman house style.

To my husband

*χάλκεα χρυσείων**

GALLIA

Chapter One

A little thought will usually show where a story begins. Gurdon considered very rightly that his began with a visit he paid to old Mrs Leighton in Cornwall Gardens. At least he knew it did not begin when he was at home, nor when he was at Rugby, nor yet when he spent two years at the Lycée in Bordeaux (though he hesitated about this part, and sometimes wondered if that had been the prologue). The interval of his life in Munich and his life in London, and again at Oxford, where he passed his examination for the Civil Service, was a barren period, with no suggestion of a story about it. But the call he had felt himself impelled to make in Cornwall Gardens, because Mrs Leighton was a connection of the Secretary of State for the Colonies, and by no means a *quantité negligeable*, had something about it of an inaugurative character, and when he looked back upon it, he perceived that this was because it had quite certainly ushered in an incident.

The incident was his journey to Paris.

'It is about Robbie,' Mrs Leighton had said, as the last visitor swept round the corner of the screen.

'Ah!'

'Yes. You will know that I do not care a rap about Robbie, although he is my only grandson – but I think of the family.'

'Just so,' said Gurdon, who knew that Mrs Leighton cared innumerable raps about Robbie, and didn't think for a second about the family. 'And what about him?'

'He is getting into the ways of wicked Paris. You know what I mean?'

Gurdon wasn't qualifying as a silent servant of his country for nothing; he didn't know in the least what she meant. He waited, looking steadily at her.

'Ah, well, you have always been so steady,' she went on, with a faint sigh, as though this were regrettable; 'but – er – Paris – the *ménage à deux*. Ah, these artists – and their models!'

Mrs Leighton was a very *rusée** and clever old lady, and her uplifted eyes as she said 'these artists', coupled with the quaint, dry twist in her voice when she said 'their models', were quite funny.

Gurdon never smiled, although perhaps Mrs Leighton meant him to. He knew the old lady's foible was to be credited with a vast knowledge of wickedness and that tenderness for the wicked which is supposed to proceed from '*tout comprendre*'.* He had heard Robbie say that the stories his grandmother could get out of one glass of Chartreuse, about the days when she was a young girl and stayed with her aunt at the French Embassy, licked anything a man could find in three times the quantity of Kümmel,* and Robbie didn't mean it as a compliment. Although he might be a bad boy, he had all that feeling of particularity about the minds of his female relatives which is an Englishman's trait as exclusive as it is touching. He was too young to perceive that, being two generations younger than his grandmother, his idea of humour must be immeasurably different. She belonged to the day when a clever woman of undoubted propriety made a reputation for wit by an audacity that was nicely calculated.

'You were not thinking of going to Paris for your holiday, perhaps?' Mrs Leighton went on, after a little pause.

Mark Gurdon was not without politeness. 'Well, in point of fact, I rather was!' he said quickly, being careful to make it seem as though she had by chance lit upon a plan he had been turning over.

It wouldn't be a bad thing for him to do Mrs Leighton any little favour, but it would have been a very bad thing if he had let her suspect that he thought he was doing her a favour.

'If you do, I wish you would just burst in upon Robbie.'

Gurdon had no difficulty in suppressing a smile at the picture Mrs Leighton had so evidently formed of her grandson's surroundings.

'Has he been exceeding his allowance?' was all he said, however.

Now, how like a man!' cried Mrs Leighton.
'Of course, if he didn't exceed his allowance, you cannot imagine that there should be anything to criticise in his way of life. Good Heavens, what a moral code!'

'My dear lady' – Gurdon began, with great deference and in defence, but he was drowned immediately.

'Let me tell you that these people are not all disastrously expensive! On the stage, in books, I grant you; but in real life – especially French real life in the neighbourhood of the studios – they are often remarkably thrifty and careful. Models, drawn from the peasant class, they have not forgotten the habits of their parents. They are not all young and pretty and fond of dress (as for that, models are never pretty in real life); they are middle-aged and plain, their minds set on *économies*, their only expense to keep a big blue bow on the neck of the odious little white dog they usually cherish!'

'My dear Mrs Leighton, your intimate knowledge' – began Gurdon, now frankly laughing, but she swept him up brusquely again.

'Of course, never tell me! Wasn't Paris my home, and don't I know it – *grille*, *entresol*, *grenier*, and *sous le toit*?'*

She made a funny little upward movement with the gold double eyeglass, and Gurdon never paused to ask himself how a life at the Embassy could have furnished so vivid an insight into these byways; he merely noticed what an *esprit* the old soul had, and what a perfect French tongue she spoke with.

He rose and held out his hand, smiling. Mrs Leighton liked Gurdon, his smiles and his silences and his appreciation; she often said to her stepsister, who, though twenty years her junior, was her great friend, 'Mark will go far.' And she did not like him less because he so obviously thought as much himself. She was old, and she knew that no man goes far who doesn't think he will go far and mean to all the time.

'You will hear from me in Paris. I foresee myself strangling that dog in its own blue bow, and pitching the lady after it into the street. But, you know, Robbie is no infant; he may have his own ideas of manly independence.'

'Robbie has no ideas of any kind,' said his grandmother with scorn – 'no ideas at all beyond *plein air** and – and that sort of thing. That is what I dislike about it. There are two ways of being vicious, my dear boy – one of them commands at least a little respect. Some men are vicious from conviction – but of the men who are vicious from convention what are you to say?' The little movement of her pretty old white hands with which she accompanied this *mot*, gave Gurdon an opportunity of kissing one of them in leave-taking. The skin felt like fine crumpled tissue-paper, and had a little breath of *fleur de limon** about it – the old French scent Mrs Leighton habitually used.

'Some from conviction, others from convention,' repeated Gurdon to himself when he got into the street. 'What a dear, queer, charming old humbug she is!'

Chapter Two

It was by means of a little blue *poste-télégraphe*** that Gurdon
announced his arrival in Paris to his old college friend Leighton,
who lived, or at anyrate had a studio, far out in the Passage des
Favorites;* and it was another little blue *poste-télégraphe* which
came to his hotel, the Lille et d'Albion in the Rue de Rivoli,*
and carried Leighton's welcome and his invitation to join him at
a certain public studio in the Latin Quarter,* where he still
studied rather fitfully.

'Dear old man, this is a rare surprise!' Leighton said, when,
later in the day, he saw the tall, English-looking figure of his
friend at the edge of the blue smoke that filled the men's studio.
They shook hands and looked at each other. They had shaken
hands last in the impossible flurry of the Oxford railway
platform, and no one who had seen them there would have
wondered that the porter followed quite another young man
with the portmanteaux, and stared wildly among fifty more in a
vain endeavour to recognise the gentleman who had engaged
him. They were like any thousand of young men at that time;
now, only two years later, they had changed immensely. Leighton's fair hair was four inches long where it had been barely
half an inch, he had a weird beard of rough tow-coloured stuff
which partially covered his white throat. He was extremely
décolleté. A horrid rag of a tie disappeared into a stained blue
waistcoat front, and a grey jacket with gaping side pockets
modelled his muscles effectively with its greasy shine. Gurdon?
Well, Gurdon looked exactly as one would have expected. He
wore a brown travelling serge,* a white shirt, and a black bow
tie. He was clean shaven, his rather hatchet-shaped face pale
and sallow, his reddish-dark hair just long enough to part in the
middle, and rigorously flattened below a brown crush hat.*

There was about him that suggestion of baths and shaves and
tailors and general precision, of which one is ashamed to feel a
little tired, because it is in itself so admirable.

'One must spend one's holiday somewhere,' Gurdon was
murmuring. 'Thought I'd look you up. Paris is always all right
for a holiday.'

'The only place in the world fit to live in, I say,' the other
replied. 'Now I'm just done. The light has been vile all afternoon, and I'm tired of sweating after the tone of that mossy old
beggar over there. I'll get my traps, and we'll come along and
have a yarn somewhere.'

Gurdon's eye travelled towards the model, whom his friend's
phrase had most aptly pictured.

'Magnificent chest and shoulders,' he said admiringly.

'Ha, ha! rather! That's old Lemuel's strong point. He travels
on that chest and shoulders, I can tell you. Here's a friend of
mine thinks you've got a *beau torse*, Lemuel, *hein*?'

A few gurgling laughs and chuckles followed this sally, and
one or two men looked up lazily at Gurdon for a moment. It
seemed to be an old studio joke, and some muttered comments
in French, American, and other foreign languages rumbled about
the studio.

The old Hercules upon the platform smiled a little, as at a
familiar compliment; without altering the pose, he seemed to
stiffen proudly; the muscles in his right arm swelled, and the
strong old fingers grasping the wooden spear contracted a trifle
more firmly. It was the end of the last hour of the afternoon,
when models get slack sometimes; and the half-jocular bit of
praise, as well as the knowledge that a stranger was looking at
him, served to brisk up the splendid old figure, on which forty
pairs of eyes had been fastened more or less all day.

'He understands English, then, does he?' Gurdon asked, with
some curiosity.

'Oh, he *is* English. Lemuel is a character, too, I can tell you.
Hasn't always been a model, by any means.'

'No, I should say not. He never developed that muscle in this
atmosphere.'

'Pretty foul, isn't it? I expect it strikes you. I'm used to it. They will smoke that *Petit Caporal*,* and that's what does it. Well, there is not any tobacco in France, anyhow.'

'I daresay you'll welcome a pound or two of the old stuff, then?'

'My dear fellow! How fearfully decent of you! You can't beat England for some things – pals and tobacco.'

They made their way into the grey and dismal little street. It was winter, but not cold. Neither of them wore an overcoat, and they stepped out briskly in the direction of the Gare Montparnasse.

They may have had a good deal to say, but they talked only in snatches. There was much cordiality in their voices, but their interests were now so different, and their lives had strayed so far apart, that there could be no consecutive talk between them all at once.

When they had struck obliquely into the Rue Vaugirard,* Leighton paused suddenly.

'I was taking you to my old barracks in the Passage,' he said, 'but I don't see the good. The light has gone, and you won't be able to see my things – that is, even if you want to.' Mark interjected something friendly. 'And I really don't see the good.'

'Well, let us consider what we are going to do tonight,' said Gurdon, noting what he imagined to be his friend's reluctance to go to the studio. That was so like Leighton – never to consider how far he was going to admit his friend to the intimacies of his new life until they were halfway to the very scene of them, then to pull up and bungle out something about the light.

In which reflection Mark utterly misjudged Robbie.

'I'm out of things here, of course. It's ages since I was in Paris. I look to you, Rob, to take me about.'

'I'll take you round,' Rob answered, with a burlesque wink. 'And I suppose you don't mean Bulliers* and that sort of haunt; you mean the Divan Japonais and the Alcazar,* eh?'

Mark nodded.

'Well, I'll have to shine out in some other togs. So we'll go to the studio, and you'll wait and look about you, while I adorn in a corner behind a wide-meshed fishing-net.'

They set out at a swinging pace, and Mark pondered. This time they didn't talk; Mark looked about him after the fashion of a man who notices things, not effects, and Leighton got all the society he wanted out of the cigar Mark had handed him at the studio door.

'How about the old lady? But I suppose you never see her much?'

'On the contrary, I sat opposite to her at dinner at the Fearons' the other night, and I have even called. She is brisker than ever, and of a freshness that shamed half the young women in the room – or should have done.'

'Say anything about me?'

'Oh, hoped I would see you when I went to Paris, and no doubt will expect me to tell her how you are getting on. She is interested in you, you know.'

'Rather; and I believe she's the only member of the family who wasn't disappointed when I turned painter. She sent for me when she heard it. She said, "Robert, you are an independent boy, and I like you. Go to Paris. Never mind what your uncle says; he doesn't know Paris. It's the only place to qualify as a human being who understands his world. Be a painter. I don't mind if you are a failure or a success, only don't give it up; stick to it and get all you can out of it. You start on Thursday? Very well. Taste all the flavours of the art life, it is very developing. I will stop your allowance from Thursday. It would never do for you to have money; you would not develop character, you would not see real life.'

Leighton had attempted some little imitation of his grand-mother's manner, and Mark roared with laughter at the climax of her advice.

'Was she as good as her word?' he asked.

'Every bit!' said Robbie, with enthusiasm. 'She's a rare old woman, and I'm proud of her. Never you believe in her wickedness; she isn't half as bad as she'd make you think, nor half as fond of the devil as she says.'

'I have no doubt that she wouldn't be hard on a man, though, if – er – if he wasn't quite straight?' Gurdon said, and looked tentatively at the houses and the evening sky.

'She abdicated her right to oversee my conduct when she stopped that four-fifty,' Robbie said, with a shrewd chirp in his voice.

Gurdon felt amazed, but volunteered no comment.

'Your uncle still holds out, I suppose?' he asked carelessly.

'Yes; he used to make up my grandmother's money to six hundred. That was in Oxford days, you remember. A daughter was not expensive, he said, and he could afford it. I should just about say he could. He was pretty sick when I made a break for Paris, but the money goes on, thank God! for it's all I have. And of course he was not bound to do anything at all, as he's only an uncle by marriage – and that with a difference. Besides, he's as close as a locked door, the worthy Hamesthwaite.'

The subject of Leighton's worldly goods dropped, and they swung along in silence for a good way.

'Now, it's not far off. I warn you, you'll be surprised when you see the kind of place I build in. Anything lonelier or less attractive – from an average point of view – than the Passage des Favorites* never was conceived by mortal architect or builder. I've often wondered *what* Favourites? Most favorites wouldn't care to live here, I take it.'

Gurdon turned a pair of hazel-grey eyes slowly upon him, but there was nothing to be made of Robbie's open face; the blue eyes looked straight before him, the lids narrowing themselves from time to time as he tasted a snatch of composition in the surrounding buildings or the street. Gurdon gave it up.

'We turn on our left sharp now.'

They had been walking about half an hour. The road was unmade and muddy, no longer a street, but a road; there were bleak gardens with dying shrubs in them, and great glass balls set up on small pillars, and heaps of shells, and stones, and coloured glass, and other excrescences of bad taste in suburban horticulture. The houses were no longer in rows, they were scattered, and occasional blank building-fields could be seen over wood palings; fields edged by a segment of a street consisting of one block of painfully narrow houses with raw edges. Over everything there was an air of neglect, of disappointed, disheartened effort, or candid squalor; it made an impression of the utmost desolation upon Gurdon, and he wondered what in heaven's name could cause a man whose very profession presupposed a love of beauty, to choose such a spot.

'Grand place for an artist this,' Leighton broke out with warm enthusiasm, and flung the end of his cigar at a broken statue which was set up behind a bush of hemlock in the garden they were passing. 'You have no idea of the queer things you see here sometimes. You'd hardly think Paris had an edge like this, would you? Over there is the *barrière*,'* waving a hand on which charcoal had formed an effective background to a turquoise set in silver, in the direction of the sunset. 'The lights that travel over this plain sometimes are magnificent. Now, for instance, look now how the thing composes! You see where they have been pulling down the backs of these houses – you see that heap of yellow sand with the puddle in the middle where they've been making mortar, and that heap of concrete there for the new façade, and the yellow freestone with the saw still in it? Look how the sun leaps into that puddle and catches hold of that saw. Jove! I've got to paint that thing one of these days.'

Gurdon felt instructed, and really did think he saw something rather fine about it.

'I shall call it "Well begun is ill done," if I send it to England; they love titles at the Academy,' Leighton went on, with the same warmth, already seeing the thing packed for delivery at a London exhibition. 'I wonder if I've got the key. Oh, perhaps Arsénie will be home by now. Here, Gurdon, stop! this is our door. Where were you off to?'

Chapter Three

'Who is Arsénie?' Gurdon asked, as lightly as he could, and smiling.

'Arsénie? Have I not mentioned her?' Leighton looked at him in frank surprise. 'Oh, she lives with me, and cooks, and looks after me, and keeps me out of mischief.' He laughed – laughed like a Paris art student.

'You're pretty well acclimatised,' Mark managed to say, with admirable carelessness, for the fact was, he had never believed a word of old Mrs Leighton's story, and with every step he took towards the Passage des Favorites it had seemed more and more improbable.

Leighton laughed again, this time with just a shade of colour in his forehead. 'You mustn't expect a great beauty. She's not that. Queer name, isn't it – Arsénie? Everybody calls her Arsenic, but that really is a bit rough.'

They had been standing at the door all this time, Robbie striking the key on the iron handle as he gave these hurried particulars. Now a step sounded inside, and the door was opened from within.

'J'amène un ami à moi, belle, mais ne te dérange pas,'* Leighton said in execrable French as they went inside.

'Tiens, bon – s'il ne veut pas manger!'* cried the woman, in a voice very shrill, but gay. She had the coarse, rough black hair of the Midi, and the sallow skin and large features, but there was a possibility of drama in her pose, of repartee upon her thick lips, and of immense practicality in her shrewd, bold eye. She looked about thirty-four as she stood there, carelessly dressed, and with no figure in particular. In point of fact, she had the most perfect classic build of any model in the Quartier. It was because she was so like Venus that she was dowdy in common clothing. There were lines of temper, and power, and dominance in her forehead. She had a small *casserole** in one hand and a spoon in the other; she was cooking the evening meal, and after she had looked at Gurdon a moment with a very direct but friendly stare, she turned back to a corner where a ridiculous little *fourneau** and charcoal stove had been accommodated.

'I could never keep out of debt in this world if I hadn't Arsénie,' said Robbie, bringing his glance from the stove to Gurdon's inexpressive face. 'I don't owe a penny, and I don't believe I've been drunk since last Mi-Carême.* If I had that four-fifty I could afford to do without her, and go to the bad – as it is, I couldn't. Hello, Lou-lou!'

A very small fluffy white dog got up from a heap of drapery in a corner, and came wagging and wriggling towards Leighton; it wore an immense blue bow upon its neck. Gurdon passed his hand over his forehead, and walked a few paces to a dark corner, where a shabby divan was constructed below a big brown barge-sail. He was a good deal perplexed.

'I shall change now, Mark; take a squint at those *croquis** over there.'

Gurdon moved nearer to the divan. It was a big, barn-like studio, and at the other end he could hear Arsénie playing with the little dog in a voice like the sharpening of a carving-knife, and with a rough show of affection that made him shudder. All round, the walls were pinned over with sketches, studies, schemes for pictures, caricatures, verses, impertinences and toys from Carnival time. On the floor a few mats were lying, and skins. All was wonderfully clean, nothing but the ashes of cigarettes lay upon the divan or the floor. A pair of wooden sabots were in a corner, a few hats hung on pegs. Gurdon made a careful inspection of these things, because he felt really interested, and he saw that his friend's hand was strong and sure, and utterly different from what it had been when he drew dons and proctors and freshers in the old days.

He turned to go over to the stove and talk to Arsénie, but at that moment she opened a little door and disappeared, striking matches, and evidently engaged in getting a light.

He pushed aside a heap of clothes on the divan, and sat down to rest a minute till she came back.

To his amazement, a head reared itself at the other end of the heap of clothing – a head with a good deal of black-brown hair cut short, and a pair of very round, very sleepy eyes; two feet thrust themselves out of his end of the bundle and swung to the floor. The figure sat and then stood up and shook herself; she seemed a girl of about eighteen.

'Qui donc?' she said, looking candidly and laughingly at Gurdon. Just then Leighton came in, hitching his shoulders into a black coat, which was less familiar to him than his grey jacket.

'Hullo, young Lemuel, you here?' he said in English.

'Yes; been asleep, though. Who is this?' She pointed to Gurdon as though she ought to be told at once of any intruder into the circle.

'Friend of mine from England, Gurdon by name. Look here, Lemuel, don't you make love to him.'

The girl leapt into the air with a high, curious shriek of amusement and delight. She was a round, well-developed creature, but she was light and fearfully agile, and it made a wonderful effect. When she descended, she cut a strange step towards Gurdon, flung both her arms round his head, and kissed him on his severe, neatly-shaven lips. Then she went off into the gayest, most squealing of laughs.

'You see how I begin,' she said, and danced over the floor and swung round and looked at them, and doubled herself up to scream and laugh again.

There was something so mocking and provoking about the creature, that Gurdon, laughing, but tingling curiously in a way he did not stop to understand, jumped up from the divan and caught her, and said –

'I'm going to box your ears, you saucy child!' He gave her two light pats on each side of her head, took her by the elbows firmly, and said, 'Now, are you sorry? Not a bit?' She was tremendously pretty. 'Will you do it again?'

'No, I just won't,' she said demurely, but with a nod of such shrewdness that Leighton fell to guffawing in the corner.

'Voyons, mes enfants – du café!' shouted Arsénie from the stove, and brought forward a little tray.

The girl they had called Lemuel flew round the studio and sat on the floor beside Robbie, pretending to laugh when she looked at Gurdon, and throwing her dress skirt over her head as she rocked about in mock paroxysms. Mark's mind was full of bewilderment as he took his place in this strange circle. Who was this wild creature, a child and not a child? How was she with Leighton and Arsénie? He looked from one to the other of them, intending to ask about her, but they were playing ball with the little white dog, and Lemuel's round eyes were peeping at him from under her skirt hem.

'I think we'd better not say who you are; you've behaved yourself so disgracefully,' Leighton just then said, looking over his shoulder. 'She is the daughter of our friend with the *beau torse*, and she is called young Lemuel.'

'Moi, aussi,' she began to scream, but Robbie put his hand out and caught her by the hair, and they played together till they nearly upset the coffee. Gurdon took up Lou-lou and fingered the beast's big bow, while he wondered what old Mrs Leighton would make of the only element that had been wanting in her picture of Robbie's surroundings.

Chapter Four

It was not only to look after Robbie Leighton, and oblige that young man's grandmother, that Gurdon had come to Paris. A notable feature of his mind was a peculiar power of forming small but effective combinations; the power was now more than a natural faculty. Mark had discovered, early in life, that he had such a quality, and he had had many opportunities of becoming impressed with a sense of its usefulness; he therefore determined to develop it as another man might decide to develop his talent for music or sculpture. On the principle that the greater includes the less, Gurdon, while capable of forming a scheme of very respectable magnitude, was also sensible of the importance of the smallest details, and made a practice of never neglecting them. You might have met Gurden anywhere – at dinner, in a train, between the acts, on a racecourse, in the cabin of a steamer – and after half-an-hour's conversation you would have put him down merely as an excellent specimen of the average man; in which judgment you would have been mistaken. For this very power I speak of is by no means part of the average man's equipment, and it was just this and nothing else that distinguished Mark from the crowd. It is very habitual to use the phrase regarding a young man that he must 'make a career for himself'; and there is nothing quite so rare as to see the young man who has done it. Circumstances, when not relatives or an accident of birth, are the usual agents in the manufacture of this article; and to come across the man who, not having either the relatives or the accident of birth, and not being favoured by the circumstances, has deliberately set to work to construct the circumstances, to connect them with the motor engine of his own will, and, having set the whole a-going, to contrive that a career shall be the result – to come across such a man is to have found something approaching the human equivalent of a blue rose.

Gurdon's father had been an engineer, and a fairly successful one, too; his mother a curate's daughter, who to the single effort of giving birth to him had added the second of selecting his Christian name, and then died. Mark always did his mother justice when he thought of her. He was far too keen and fair-minded not to see that she had done very well by him; she had given him a splendid constitution, a very nice nose, which was not too suggestive of talent to be handsome and even aristo-cratic, and a very useful kind of name. She might just as easily have called him Jeremiah – for she was the daughter of a Low-Church curate who still read in the Old Testament, and had brought his daughter up to do likewise. He knew that he owed a great deal to his mother, and he forgave her handsomely, since on the whole it lay very flat, for the fine and slightly rippled hair which had also been of her bestowal. There is nothing in his personal appearance that a man resents more fiercely than a tendency to curl or crinkle in his hair.

His father's was a life of change and chance. Sometimes there was more money than at other times, and it had been in one of their brightest moments that young Mark's four years at Rugby were paid for. Then came the French experience, and while his father held a post as manager of some extremely expensive and complicated wine-pressing machinery, Mark had crossed the Bordeaux Jardin Public four times daily, on his way to and from the Lycée. French, even when acquired in Bordeaux, is a tremendous arrow in a young man's quiver when he comes to shoot at a mark in the world; and young Gurdon took to it like a duck to water, and all his life would drop into a French book for preference; and, having sat through one fortnight of perfor-mances at the Français,* arose and left the building with an exquisitely chastened accent, which never forsook him. Even as it is customary to look for no grit in the schoolboy who keeps his nails clean, so the morals of the Englishman who speaks French like a native are very justfiably doubted by people of experience; but on both these points an exception may perhaps be claimed in favour of Mark. When Gurdon, senior, was sent to put up and superintend certain brewing plant at Munich, his son naturally accompanied him, and thereupon set himself to conquer first his intuitive antipathy to the Germans, and then his no less fierce objection to their declensions, with the result that his midday Bairisch suited him as well as his previous Médoc had done, and he thought out for himself, combining an immense dispassionateness with the hot logical fervour of two-and-twenty, the Franco-German question,* to his own complete consequeı.t peace of mind in this matter.

The Munich life appearing for the time a permanency (if such a misuse of terms be forgivable), Mark came to England and to Oxford with an education so peculiar, and in some respects so in advance of that of men of his age, that he felt moderately certain of making his exams, for his chosen career, and entering the Civil Service with good numbers.* He found he had to work harder than he had expected, but, nevertheless, events fell out to his satisfaction, and his first reverse came after he had acquired a much-yearned-for stool in the Colonial Office. It was the death of his father. All Mark's life had been so matter of fact thus far, that he was dismayed to find how much he regretted the man who, in life, had meant very little to him. He put on his decorously correct mourning with a puzzled brow, and then went to look after the investment of the £1500 which was all the money he had to expect as capital. His father had been his only relative; he was now alone in the world – without the least sense of loneliness; the curious sadness that would fall upon him when he laid down the afternoon paper, when he waited for the next course of the abominable club dinner, when he looked across the water in St James's Park towards that circle of buildings in which his hopes and his future lay – seemed to him inexplicable, because illogical. But in time the sadness wore away, and only the puzzled remembrance of it stirred sometimes in his brain.

It was characteristic of Mark that he invested that £1500 as it stood.

'There may be a time when I shall want just such a sum of

money for some particular step in my career,' he told himself; and perhaps he phrased it, There shall be a time, and not, There may be.

And then the dull months went over, painted only by the minute social advances the young man made. The friendship of Robbie Leighton had introduced him to a circle which ideally represented the desire of his very wide-awake dreams; this might be looked upon as one of the adventitious circumstances mentioned before, but how many young men could have made any capital out of a single afternoon call, with a number of other people in the room?

It was Mark's own cleverness that told him to make a conversational opportunity, not for himself, but for his brilliant hostess – and to make it in French. When he thought over the visit, he discovered that beyond 'How do you do?' and 'Good-bye,' it was his unique utterance in that drawing-room; but it drew from Mrs Leighton a very delightful sort of command to Robbie to tell Gurdon to call upon her, and Mark never misled himself as to its importance.

So much for Mark's character; his appearance has been indicated. As to his belief, it was concretely rooted in himself, and his creed was that it behoved a man – not every man, but such a man as himself – to succeed. Success on the one hand implies a failure somewhere or of some one on the other. Mark quite saw the admirable justice of this. Some people of course had to fail, it was what they were intended for and it suited them, only he was not of these. He was born to be a successful, honourable, gentlemanly, 'decent' kind of fellow; just as some men were born to be low, ruffianly devils, or seedy, pitiable failures. As he had a decidedly kind heart, and wouldn't have hurt a fly, he thought it fearfully hard on them, and would like to have given them each a sovereign, poor chaps. This, in rough outline, was Mark's ethics.

So he stood, fresh and handsome, on the steps of the Lille et d'Albion, pulling on a pair of French Suède gloves, and prepared to pursue his second object in coming to Paris. It was about eleven o'clock, so he stepped out for Neal and a glimpse of yesterday's *Times*; at twelve it would be time to look up some of the men at the Embassy; they would have had time to address about five envelopes apiece, and would be ready for luncheon. In the afternoon he was going to Auteuil* to see St Crispin, the marvellous colt belonging to his friend the Marquis de Mont Voisin, come in fourth, that being the place assigned inevitably to young Mont Voisin's horses. He owed this very desirable acquaintance also to Mrs Leighton. The old Marquise having been a friend of her girlhood, it was natural that, when the boy came to London, she should have made a little dinner for him, and collected such young men as she thought he would like to meet. Mont Voisin spoke just as little and just as much English as every other Frenchman, and it had fallen to the lucky Gurdon to show him London, and answer all his questions in his own tongue. A card discreetly left at the Hôtel Mont Voisin on his way to Leighton at the studio had procured for Gurdon a cordial invitation to 'team down'* (this was how Mont Voisin put it, and it is certain he imagined himself to be employing an extremely showy bit of London slang) on his coach.

Now it was an annoying thing to Gurdon that, as he conscientiously read his *Times*, there should crop up continually the insufferable remembrance of that half-hour in Leighton's studio. For one thing, the cropping-up of recollections was not what he was accustomed to expect of his own mind; for another, they interfered materially with the digest of the South African intelligence which he was bent on making. It was part of Gurdon's daily routine to read first the news of the great Empire whose ends he was called upon in the humblest of fashions to serve, then to think about them, and finally to know what he thought about them. He had the clearest possible head. One thing at once, and that thing thoroughly, was his role; but if a man is to be disturbed by the recurrence of an atmosphere, such as the atmosphere of the studio, and that atmosphere accompanied by a sensation, such a sensation as the insolent kiss of a minx of a girl, how in the world is he to reflect upon the rights and wrongs of the Swazis?* Gurdon had barely got rid of this problem when he set out for the Legation.

Chapter Five

'Hullo, that can't be! By Jove, it is though! I say, here comes Miss Essex.'

The two men wele walking across the Jardin du Luxembourg* after a *déjeuner* at the Hôtel Foyot,* for which Gurdon had paid an exceedingly round number of francs, and it was of course Robbie Leighton whose careless youth still expressed itself in a number of such ejaculations. Gurdon saw a tall girl coming towards them in the sunshine that filtered through the plane trees; he noticed that she was fair and slim and English; he moved his stick into his other hand, so as to be ready to take his hat off; and he also observed the light and colour that seemed to overspread his friend's face. As for Robbie, he saw the pompons of the planes patterned black upon a pale sky dappled in opaline colours of winter clearness; he heard the firm, sharp beat of her slim feet upon the orange path, and felt something severe and virginal and beautiful in her walk; and then he swept his hat from his head in an ardour of smiles, which was made very noticeable by the correct courtesy of Gurdon's gesture. The next instant both men came to a halt, brief enough, but sharp and simultaneous, amazement, in a dull colour of mounting blood, painting itself in their faces. The girl had cut Leighton dead. It had been clear, intentional, and effective. The pale, fair face had seemed a little paler as she passed them by, the clear blue eyes had fixed a quiet gaze between their shoulders.

'In God's name!' began Leighton rather gaspingly, as they settled into a vacant seat – 'In God's name, what can she mean?'

'You appear to have mistaken the lady,' Gordon said, with a faint sarcasm below the lightness of his tone.

'Mistaken her? Well, if anything was plain, it was that she *knew* me! What in the world has happened?'

'Did you say Essex? Not the sister of Dark Essex, of Balliol, by any chance?'

'By every certainty. Last year he wrote and told me she was coming out, and asked me to be of use to her in any way I could. I have been of use to her in a hundred ways, and we've been the best of friends ... Some brute has been telling lies about me!' Leighton wound up in a voice of sudden passion.

'Or perhaps the truth?' Gurdon had the kind of personal courage which can say a little thing like that.

'Oh, you mean – Arsénie?'

Their eyes met as Leighton turned and looked at Mark. It appeared to be an opportunity to get at his friend's mind on this subject; it appeared to be the moment for doing Mrs Leighton a favour.

'My dear fellow,' Gurdon began in expostulatory cordiality, 'this art circle of yours up here is a very small thing, and it is not to be expected that the light of day is to be screened off from one especial building in the Passage des Favorites. What in the world have you hoped for? Did you mean these people who frequent the same studio as yourself all day, not to know this thing? Really, Leighton, you are not going to tell me you were not prepared for an incident of this kind?'

'Prepared for it?' cried Robbie. 'Prepared to have Margaret Essex cut me as though I were a blackguard not fit to be spoken to, or to have her eyes rest on? Would *you* have been prepared for it?'

Leighton was snorting with indignation and a sense of out-raged virtue.

'Of course I should have been; always supposing I could have contrived so idiotic a situation for myself. You can't reckon without public opinion and people's idea of life. Such women as Miss Essex are public opinion, and while they inhabit the same part of Paris as yourself, you must count them in your schemes. Why should Miss Essex's views be any different here from what they would be in London?'

Leighton sank together in a dismayed and perplexed heap, and Mark continued to talk over the ruins without apparently noticing the havoc he was causing. 'It must be one thing or the other, and you have to choose which,' he concluded presently, after a monologue to which Robbie had given gloomy and disgusted attention. 'Besides, I know the sort of woman Miss Essex is; it was written all over her – in her walk, her face, the swing of her gown.' Poor Robbie had only read the poetry of these elements. 'You can't mistake them. Made of a very fine material, but cold and inhuman as the grave itself.' He leaned back complacently, folding his arms. 'Measuring all men with a measure, and that measure made of wrought steel.'

'Rot!' said Leighton simply, and with that got up, and made as though to pursue his way towards the studio.

There was a silence of several minutes. Even when they paused again while Gurdon bought a couple of bunches of violets at the gate of the Jardin, no word was spoken.

It was Leighton who broke the silence, and his voice was careless and gay again. 'We'll go and sit in the courtyard and have a yarn with old Lemuel; he isn't sitting today, and you'll find him a queer old chap.' The meeting with Miss Essex was not apparently to colour the whole afternoon, and Gurdon caught himself wondering how deep it had gone with Leighton. 'I thought so; there he is, lifting weights just to show off to the men.'

The old Hercules was dressed in seedy black, wearing a sombrero which made him handsomer and more picturesque than ever. He had a couple of big iron bars in his hands with balls at the ends of them, and he was raising these above his head and twirling them in the air. Gathered round him, just outside the sculpture studio, upon the greenish-grey flagstones, were some of the men students, waiting for the afternoon work to begin. It was a Monday afternoon, and the broad stone steps that led down into the courtyard were covered with Italians, women in garish aprons, head-cloths, and skirts; men, in more or less ragged everyday clothes, carried bundles which contained costumes of various sorts. Children, all with immense black eyes in gingerbread-coloured faces, tumbled about like guinea-pigs, sang and screamed, or were portentously still and silent, according as they were accompanied by an elder sister of some nine summers or not.

To the outsider it was a very picturesque scene. To the student it was Monday afternoon.

'You must have been painted an immense number of times, Mr Lemuel, you're so completely the classic type,' Gurdon said politely to the old man, who had put down his weights and was wiping his broad, fine brow.

'Well, I may say I have!' the Hercules replied, in a remarkably small, insignificant voice. 'Munkacszy's* design for the ceiling of an audience hall at the Champ de Mars last year – I was the Zeus in that. You will have seen Laurent's* fresco at the Panthéon? I am there. I posed for three figures there and for the head of one. Oh, and in the last ten years – yes! That group of the new Ajax – if you were at the Salon three years ago, you might have seen it – it created a great sensation, because poor young Suvain shot himself beside it on varnishing day; it was his, you know, and they hadn't given him the place he expected. I worked seven months with him for that. It was a grand thing.'

Insensibly, as they talked, they had been moving in the direction of the street, and before he knew it, Mark found himself pushing open the swing-door of the *marchand de vin* at the corner.

'But before this part of your career, what were you engaged in?' he asked, after little glasses had been handed them.

'Ah, before that I was a sculptor myself, and slapped clay with as good a will as any.'

The old man's face darkened, and his small voice sounded as though the Amer Picon* had got into it too.

'But I never made anything of it, and I had a wife and family to keep.'

Good heavens! it was this man's daughter, Gurdon remembered.

'And so many asked me to pose – for high terms too – that I saw I could do better at it.'

Mark suspected a fine talent for idleness in this powerful old

Jove, but he only said, 'Sculpture ought to be a fine thing for the muscles.'

'Ah, my muscles were made before ever I saw a mallet or dreamed of touching one. You must make the muscles when they're young, sir, and they'll never quite disappear. Boxing made mine, when I was at the University. A performer with the gloves yourself, perhaps?'

Gurdon said he was fond of it, but more for the exercise than the science.

'I lead a fairly sedentary life – I'm in a Government office – and I find an hour three times a week keeps me wonderfully fit,' he added in a conversational way, and perhaps impelled to give some confidence about himself as a means of putting himself on an equality with the old man.

'It is long since I darkened those doors,' old Lemuel said, slowly and musingly. 'Who knows, you may be sitting in the same seat.'

'You were – ?' Gurdon began in some surprise.

The white head nodded slowly several times. Gurdon got the idea that the Paris model did not wish to talk about those days. He was wrong: there was nothing old Lemuel didn't want to talk about.

'I had a sort of an ambition once – oh, I've seen the folly of it long since – and it was out of place there.'

This made Mark uncomfortable. He called sharply to have their glasses filled again, and, with his brows knitting, quickly asked Lemuel what he meant?

'Well, I wanted to get on, you see; the whole thing was too slow for me. I'd no money and precious little interest, and – I wanted to marry.' He stopped, but Gurdon accepted this pause in silence, and, after putting his lips to his glass, the old model went on musingly. 'Yes, I wanted to marry; ah, it's a very long while ago, that! I had energy, I had some push about me then. A salary on a crawling scale, with a pension at the end of it, seemed to me too poor a thing to sit down and wait for. I thought I might do something to get myself into notice. What was the use of my being one of hundreds whose names were unknown except to their immediate superiors in office and to the hall porter? A mere coral insect, one of thousands, raising a mountain reef of pink tape!'

Mark's lips folded themselves in and yet more tightly in. He was young enough, although twenty-eight years of age, to be surprised, to imagine something of a coincidence about his meeting with this man, about the similarity in his own feelings now and that other Government clerk's then. He looked rather fixedly at old Lemuel's physique, the set of his neck upon his shoulders, the pose of his head. He imagined him young; to look at he must have been a man in a thousand; his manner, too, was smooth, easy, and dignified. Years of being bandied about in a studio had given little unfamiliar touches of servility to it in places; but these still struck oddly and incongruously upon the ear, and in no wise seemed natural to the man. Had not old Lemuel of the *beau torse* and the Paris studios had more in his favour thirty years ago than he, Gurdon, at this moment? Mark was not by any means a man of sentiment; it was not so much that he despised it as that it was the very last attitude his mind was likely to assume, but no human being can be wholly without this impractical quality, and Gurdon had, of course, a little of it – so little that it was just enough for himself. His clear head showed him that the points in which he was superior to the young man Lemuel must once have been, were not upon the surface, were not easily discoverable. And the conversation made the more dent upon his brain, because, only the evening before, driving home upon the box-seat of Mont Voisin's coach, he had thought to himself, 'I am not getting on.' With the upper octave of his brain he was discussing with the Marquis the breed of English racehorses and the inferiority of French blood; then there had come rushing to him on the sharp wind that tightened the skin upon his face, this sudden thought, 'I am not getting on,' and at once the deeper octave had played with variations upon this theme. Mark had had a socially successful afternoon, following upon a socially successful luncheon; if he had been thinking about himself at all, he might have been thinking that on the whole he was doing very fairly well. But he liked racing, and he liked Mont Voisin's Paris chatter, and he had not been thinking about himself at all. Then the evening breeze had brought him that uncomfortable thought; so clear and crisp and definite, that it had the effect upon him of the utterance of a being who knows better than one's self. An argumentative fellow in the main, Mark didn't argue with this impersonal dictum; he tried his best to discover upon what collocation of half-liquid ideas it had been based, but he could trace none of these, although he searched and filtered his brain to the utmost.

Failing this, he had set himself to sum up his position, and had, so to speak, heaved a mental log to determine by dead reckoning at least his rate of professional progress. A very few minutes served to show him that the dictum could be justified. What would the next year bring him, in all likelihood? At the best, if the Government held on, chance might put him ahead of some senior. His chief, Lord Hamesthwaite, might perceive him more nearly, might suspect his ability, might differentiate him, in his own mind, from his fellows. Ah, how much that differentiation would mean! That was, at the best, the very best. At the worst? At the worst, he would dine out a little oftener, meet a few more important people, be caught up to the paradise of Lady Hamesthwaite's Wednesday dinners. That was all. Quite certainly he was not getting on.

The thoughts engendered by that dictum were in no way dissipated or diluted in their discomforting strength by an evening at the theatre. A morning at the Cluny and Panthéon,* which he had always previously failed to see, and to which Leighton now dragged him – these also were powerless to lead his thoughts from a more or less profitless contemplation of his own future. Now, having chanced against a queer old studio-character, that the conversation should take this very turn, and his companion appear in the shocking character of a disappointed appointment-seeker, with a background which, in a tray full of human experiences, could not be distinguished from his own, was sufficiently disquieting. The thoughts set flowing by old Lemuel's brief confidences had so absorbed Mark's attention that he missed even a sentence or two of the slow, musing talk.

The soft, small voice of the man, his fixed eyes, the backward throw of his big head, with its cover of shining white curls and tangles – all these things made up the impression that he was unwinding his thoughts from the silver cobwebs of the past.

'Get to know something – yes, that is the scheme, I was right so far – get to know something – and don't print it. The mistake was that I did.'

It was this phrase, very emphatically spoken, which captured and led back Gurdon's excursive mind. He was just going to put a question, when the door burst open and Leighton came in with a rush.

'Gad, I thought as much!' he exclaimed, shouldering up to them past a group of blue cotton *ouvriers*.* 'When in doubt as to old Lemuel's whereabouts, try the wine-shop, eh?' He caught the old man a whack on his big shoulder, and laughed as he ordered a little glass for himself.

When the *Marmorweib** of romantic legend felt the first pink shaft of morning sunlight on her stony bosom, the life that night and the green moonbeams had given her stopped suddenly, and so long as the sun shone she was cold upon her pedestal. This change meant a moment of keen pain for her, we may fancy. There was a blasting touch of the morning about young Leighton and his greeting, and it wrought some such change in old Lemuel. On Gurdon, too, it was not lost. Something forbade him saying, 'We were speaking of early days,' or anything of the kind. He was silent. The whole foregoing conversation began to seem unreal and shadowy. It was to be remembered often at other times; but now he listened with an odd expression in his face as Robbie announced that he was off work for the afternoon; the new model was too vile for anything, and he wasn't going to paint her. No modelling, just a hundredweight or two of *Frankforterwurst* without the spice.

'Look here, I'll make a sketch of you instead, if you like. There's a line in your jaw that I like rather.'

'All right. How long will it take?' asked Mark.

'Oh, depends; say an hour or two, and then we'll go over the river and dine. Lemuel, can we go up to your place? There's a

very fair light there, and I don't suppose little Lem will think it
an intrusion.'

'She's not at home, she's sitting for Carlo Deo's wood-nymph.
You're very welcome.'

In a few minutes they were mounting the five flights to the old
model's *appartement*.

Chapter Six

The twenty years between Mrs Leighton and her stepsister, Lady Hamesthwaite, made no sort of difference to their friendship, which was of the closest possible kind, but it would have been very difficult for an outsider to discover in what the very distinct bond between the two women consisted.

It is almost unusual for relations to come into any such close connection as will make them deep and lasting friends. But, a good way back in Julia Hamesthwaite's life, there had been a moment at which Mrs Leighton had played the part of a friend, rather than that of a half-sister, and the younger woman never forgot it. She owed her very excellent marriage to Mrs Leighton; or, to speak more clearly, she owed her escape from a very unfortunate marriage to that sympathising and clever woman. The incident has nothing to do with this story, and need not be detailed. But Lady Hamesthwaite, fitted in every way to be the wife of a distinguished servant of the Crown, had as nearly as possible missed this brilliant vocation, and she owed it to her half-sister that she had not quite missed it.

The intercourse between the house in Cornwall Gardens and the house in Grosvenor Place was very constant and very cordial, and it was to be expected that, the very afternoon of the Hamesthwaites' return to London from their country place, Mrs Leighton should have looked in to greet her sister Julia.

'And you know I have Gallia* with me,' Lady Hamesthwaite had said, as they sat over their tea in the smallest of the tiresomely immense drawing-rooms which seemed fitted for nothing but big political receptions. 'It is not often that I am so fortunate.' A little laugh followed this remark; it was certainly remarkably seldom that this mother and daughter could be found together.

'I hope she is in, and that she will be coming down. I take the deepest interest in Gallia,' Mrs Leighton said quickly.

'You know that you are a little responsible for her peculiarities; it was you who advised me always to let her have her own way, and dispose of herself as she pleased.'

'It was my advice for the time being; you would have done no good by thwarting Gallia when she chose her path years ago. She has been lost to us both since then.'

Lady Hamesthwaite hastened to cover with a smile the sigh that involuntarily escaped her.

'But – I think Gallia will come home. My theory is that the modern girl has also a crop of wild oats to sow; not the usual sort, of course – *Dieu soit béni** – but wild oats nevertheless. Perhaps she will have finished soon, and then, you will see, Gallia will come home.'

There was confidence and reassurance always to be found in Mrs Leighton's remarks. She had lived a long time with her eyes open and seen many things, and she was usually right in what she predicted.

The little pause that fell between the two women was broken in upon by a step crossing the parquet of an adjoining floor; a second later Gallia Hamesthwaite appeared beside a curtained archway.

'How do you do, Aunt Celia?' she said, coming to kiss the old lady on the cheek.

Mrs Leighton took both her hands, and smiled up at her with a penetrative and slightly interrogative smile.

Whether she was satisfied or not with the inspection did not appear. It had the effect of annoying Gallia excessively. She turned to her mother.

'Have the afternoon papers come yet?'

'I don't know, dear, but ring and ask Bowles; they are usually sent up to my dressing-room, you know.'

'Do you not think mother looking very well?' Gallia began, after she had rung the bell. 'I do; I can't imagine why she should come rushing up here now, of all times in the year, when London never fails to give her that bronchial trouble.'

'Her social duties, my dear –' Mrs Leighton began.

'But she has no social duties. Of course, if she were anyone else, and I were someone quite different, she would have to get me married and all that, but as it is – Come, it must be admitted that I have lifted the burden of social duties pretty thoroughly off mother's back. Thank you; but, Bowles, please send out for the other papers, and bring them to me when they come.'

A very few minutes later she retired to the window with a sheaf of journals, and was entirely lost to the conversation at the other side of the room.

'Do you think she is on the way home?' asked Lady Hamesthwaite a little wistfully.

'She is still very young, and proportionately earnest. She will slough this skin in time, but one always fears a little what skin will be found underneath.'

The crackle of the newspapers at the window covered the clear, precise tones of Mrs Leighton's voice, and Gallia read on undisturbed.

'Anything of interest, darling?' Lady Hamesthwaite called out presently.

'Yes, there is some rather good correspondence about – but you wouldn't care to hear about it.'

'Tell us what is interesting you, dear Gallia,' her Aunt Celia said, with bland encouragement.

Gallia did not lay down her paper, but in a tone of level indifference replied, 'There is an agitation about the State regulation of vice.'*

'My *dearest* child!' 'Dear Gallia!' came from the ladies on the sofa.

'But I don't suppose it will come to anything. One man very justly observes that the result of it has been the abolition of regulation, not the abolition of vice. I wonder who he is. He writes rather well.'

Mrs Leighton got up and went over to the window with her soft, elegant step; she put the fine crinkled hand Gurdon had kissed upon the girl's head, and sank upon the other end of the settee.

'Dear Gallia, I'm not an illiberal old woman, now am I?' she said, with a delightfully light French note in her voice.

Gallia looked quietly into her face.

'I hardly know. I'm not good at summing up people, Aunt Celia.'

'Well, I will make you a little proposition, and you shall judge at the end of it if I am illiberal in my opinions.'

Gallia's lip curled to a smile – a very old smile for so young a face.

'Ah, you are going to say –'

'I think you will find I am not going to say that,' Mrs Leighton interrupted humorously. 'I am not going to say it is not a fit subject for you to read about or think about. I am only going to suggest that it is a waste of time – your valuable time' – her voice was very serious now – 'to make up your mind upon so exceedingly complicated a subject as this one,' tapping the paper with her taper old fingers, 'for the simple reason that you are unable to assist its settlement one way or the other! That's all. Now?'

'But, auntie, how can you say I am unable to assist its settlement? I can't make the State do this or that – I couldn't even cause father to support a Bill – but I, in my own person, must read about and think about it, because it is a question that only girls can settle ultimately.'

Mrs Leighton was infinitely too tactful to demur to this sweeping statement. She paused for a moment, trying to think what it would be best to say.

'One likes to know the amount of one's indebtedness to people,' Gallia went on, without enthusiasm, but simply and firmly. 'I could not be happy – I mean that I could not have a feeling of self-respect – unless I had estimated just the amount of my debt to that class of society which assures my class a good deal of its immunity.'

There was a terrible, portentous pause.

'I think, dear, if you knew how much phrases of that kind can hurt and distress other women who have – who have striven to play their part of wife and mother well, you would perhaps reserve them.'

It was Lady Hamesthwaite who came up and made this very gentle remark, through the curls that hung over her daughter's ear. Then she dropped a kiss upon the curls and moved away through the big drawing-rooms.

Gallia flew after her and caught her, and rubbed away the two tears that were pausing at the top of the pretty, delicately-coloured cheeks.

'Dearest mother, don't *you* misunderstand me, for Heaven's sake! I was a fool to speak as I did to Aunt Celia – one always is a fool to say what one thinks about *anything* – but you know, mother, I never trouble you with my views upon these, or any other of the subjects that puzzle me. Whoever they may concern, they do not touch *you* in the very least! How you can have found any offence to yourself, in your – in your delightful position, in what I said, beats me altogether. I wasn't talking about wives and mothers – I was talking about – '

'Don't, dear Gallia! it distresses me so much!'

'I wasn't going to say anything then, I wasn't really!' Gallia explained, with childlike eagerness. 'I only want to say that wives and mothers were as far from my thoughts as pigs and whistles. I won't attempt to tell you what I did mean. I won't refer to it again. Auntie Celia is not like you; she pretends to know the world! – yes, she has, I know, she has lived a very long time in it in a measure – and she leads me into argument, and then I am idiot enough to say what I think, and sometimes idiot enough to refer to something that is true! But never mind that; it shan't happen again if I can help it. Only, mother, don't you be distressed. I *can't bear* that. Do me the justice, mother, to say I don't bother you with such subjects,' she pleaded in genuine distress, and with the most single-minded pursuit of her subject, she blundered into yet another pitfall, as youth will.

'I never, never confide any difficult thoughts to you on the subjects over which I am really puzzling – now do I?'

Unlike her sister, Lady Hamesthwaite had no great sense of

humour, or she would have noted the pathetic absurdity of her daughter's apology for having hurt her feelings. As it was, she saw and felt the pathos of the stab conveyed in this last remark, which Gallia was so eager to drive home, but not the absurdity of her doing so at such a moment. It was but too true that Gallia never confided to her mother the thoughts that really occupied her extraordinary brain, and that such peace of mind as Lady Hamesthwaite enjoyed regarding her daughter sprang from this very reserve.

'I am angry with Aunt Celia for driving me into saying such things before mother! It was abominable of me to do it, anyhow. I have broken my record that I meant so hard to keep. I always recognised mother's unfitness for any discussion of serious moral problems, and yet the first worldly-minded old woman who comes along with a cambric bandage for my weasel eyes, irritates me into wounding mother with an expression of my views about realities. It's too disgusting. It's shown me how little self-control I've got, so it may do good that way; but – I'm angry with Aunt Celia all the same.'

In some such channel as that Gallia's thoughts were running when her mother had kissed her and smiled before rejoining Mrs Leighton.

'I wonder, is there anything so difficult as to be a good mother now-a-days? 'Lady Hamesthwaite said, with a sad little smile, as she felt her sister's arm go round her waist with a comforting pressure. 'But you must forgive dear Gallia,' she went on quickly, with that beautiful instinct of protection that few mothers seem to be without, in spite of their growing difficulties and trials. 'She is exceedingly penitent about her want of tact. Gallia has a great feeling for tact, and – and for propriety. I know she is really grieved to have introduced so unsuitable a topic.'

Mrs Leighton could not forbear a smile.

'If one had any doubt as to what century one were living in, it would be cleared up by the occurrence of such an incident as this!' she said, with the little light French turn in her voice again. 'What is dear Gallia penitent about? About having discussed an impossible subject before her mother! Ah, once it was another way, and we had to whisper behind our fans for fear the shell ears of little daughters caught a murmur of the coarse tide of life. *Ay de mi*!* which is better – or which is worse? But you are right, Julia – Gallia is still a long way from home.'

'I think – although I don't understand her – still I think that my sympathy is of use to her. I began a long time ago to let her go her own way. I cannot draw back now. Sometimes it seems long to wait for her, but I have never lost her love, and even her curious care of me is very sweet sometimes. Yes, I know she will come back some day.'

'You are the sweetest mother-woman in the world, my Julia,' Mrs Leighton said, kissing her, and noticing with apprehension a moisture in her own carefully-pencilled eyes. 'Goodbye, dear. Don't forget you and Gerald are dining with me on Thursday. Would Gallia come, I wonder? If she will, I shall be delighted. Let me know in the morning, and another man shall be found.'

'She may come home,' Mrs Leighton said reflectively, as she lay back in her victoria,* 'but I fear she'll find veal a rather insipid staple after the modern style of husk.'

Gallia stood at the window, watching the carriage drive away; her mother had left the room with Mrs Leighton, and had not returned to it. Gallia was alone with the supremely uncomfortable feeling not uncommon with her.

To look at, Gallia Hamesthwaite was no ordinary girl, but her mind and character were by no means very uncommon. She was dark and tall and slender; if her expression had been simpler, she would have been extremely attractive. Her face might have been called beautiful, by reason of the skin, hair, and eyes – particularly her skin, which was, perhaps, perfect. But a girl of far less natural beauty would have been twice as attractive, both to men and women of average taste. Gallia's very expression was one we are beginning to know, and, if the truth must be confessed, to resent a little. A young, healthy girl, with good features, good temper, good nature, and good faith, is so delightful an object, and so welcome in the world, that we are selfishly annoyed when charming-looking girls abdicate their right to these qualities, and refuse the pleasure and satisfaction that results from their contemplation. For her height, Gallia's face and head were classically little, but they made the strongest impression of divergence from the ideal of girlhood. Her eyes were clouded with wonder upon wonder about matters which have strained the strongest and toughest brains the world has ever seen. Her brows forgot to wear the smile-wreaths we have thought becoming to her years, and knitted themselves with painful intensity in contemplation of some misty peak of Darien.*

All this was the result of her particular sort of education on her particular nature.

Up till the age of seventeen, Gallia had received the best form of home education. The time that some girls devote to music, she had devoted to languages, and knew three very well, besides her own. She had absorbed the same amount of geography, history, science, and mathematics that most clever girls do absorb now-a-days, and none of it had interested the individual part of her brain. Natural sciences had arrested her most, and then, unassisted and unadvised, she made excursions in sociology, and became enraptured. Social ethics captured her; Mill and Herbert Spencer, whom she skimmed over like a swallow, fired and delighted her. A year or two later, just when she was to have come out, she went to Oxford. Her mother and her father regarded this departure with dismay. The daughters of Lady Hamesthwaite's friends never wanted to do anything of the kind: why should Gallia? Gallia was essentially a middle-class creature; her father's father had been a business man, her mother, the daughter of a monumentally successful London physician. Both these grandparents had made places for themselves in society owing to the possession of something society had not got, that mixture of energy and the instinct of success and advancement.

The girls who came to call with their mothers on Lady Hamesthwaite – who might have been, in the nature of things, Gallia's companions – were utterly remote from her. Sleek creatures, with small ears, long oval faces, narrow-fronted mouths, and smooth-netted heads, they sat there in their neat, stupidly-imagined clothes, and were coldly conscious of their unlikeness to Gallia. This girl's free movements, free play of feature, free mode of thought, free mode of dress – this last brought to better perfection than all the rest because more easily understood – made up an enigma which their blood rather than their brains divined.

Gallia had developed late; at seventeen she was a tall girl rather than a young woman; thus her head was older than her body, and had already acquired a brisk, boyish habit of thought. When femininity descended upon her, there was a struggle; she did not want it; was prepared to do without it; found it an added source of puzzlement to life, which was already a hotbed of complications for her; and, as all late-developed women do, resented it fiercely; fought separately and subdued every sign of it.

As a child, Gallia had never had a doll; had never played at keeping house, teaching school, having callers, as most other girl-children do. If there was a baby about, she had shivered and left the room. Nothing terrified her like the society of young married women. The least mention of the semi-prurient subjects so many women, and even the best-bred women, habitually discuss, sent her from the scene. In like manner she disdained as vulgar, though she was not frightened by, every sign of coquetry in girls; if she had had girl friends, she could never, save mockingly and with a curling lip, have listened to love-confidences. She adored animals, and they were her nearest companions; she doted on natural history, and studied the strange characteristics of different beasts with astonishing zest: yet she was so young and raw and contradictory, that the broad facts of nature, if applied to herself, revolted her to sickness. She aroused a certain amount of admiration in the world, but no word of love had been whispered to her even at twenty years of age, when she had been some time a freelance at Oxford.* Such is an outline of her character, no uncommon one, as I said before. There are a great many Gallias in the world nowadays, and they are, for the most part, very unhappy people.

Chapter Seven

'So this is who you are?' A dark, tall, thin young man, with a very handsome face, was offering his arm to Gallia Hamesthwaite on the evening of Mrs Leighton's dinner-party, and he made this remark in a tone of insolence so effective and attractive that the girl coloured curiously, and replied to him with a look of concentrated dislike; dislike and something else as well. The man passed over the dislike, and laughed scornfully at the other ingredient, which did not seem to surprise him.

'I pardon your astonishment at discovering my parentage,' she said lightly. 'But you may consider me a sport; we can't all take after our parents, and clever people may have stupid children.' Gallia hated to find that annoyance, or some other feeling, was making her a little unnatural.

'I fail – as usual – to apprehend the drift of your remarks; my mind is ill fitted to appreciate such subtleties. But a longing for justice is ever present with me. My opinion of you is of little moment, but I had never imagined you so fatuous a person as the man I discover to be your father.'

Mr Essex – it was the very man whom Gurdon had referred to as Dark Essex of Balliol – let his words dribble forth with an amount of affectation almost too dazzling even in the Fellow of a college.

'You have dropped your serviette already,' he added, handing it to her. 'Don't keep on doing it, please. Should one eat the soup, here? I have only lunched with Mrs Leighton before.'

Gallia reassured him about the soup, and made absolutely no defence of her father. She let her eyes wander round the table to see who composed her aunt's party, for the Hamesthwaites had been the last arrivals, and dinner being announced very soon, she had only time to notice Dark Essex at the other end of the room, and establish her composure before he came to take her in. Although she looked about the table, and went to work naturally enough with her dinner, she was, in reality, palpitating with anxiety to hear his next remark. She had come to know this man at Oxford, at some lecture, a little over a year ago. Their meetings had been very irregular, and characterised by some peculiarity. Essex was as reactionary as his kind of man always is, and he had never before come upon a woman without a trace of coquetry in her. He didn't believe in such a woman as a possibility. He was forced to converse in her own key with Gallia, but he liked to use her roughly at the same time. Once he had taken her out in his boat, and they had spent at least four hours together. Another time he had come upon her out on a long walk in the direction of Abingdon, when he too was going the same way, and they had gone along together. Once at Abingdon, it seemed necessary to have some tea, and then there was no particular occasion to hurry back, and it was nine o'clock before they reached Oxford.

When he forgot all his assumed rudeness of manner, he could be charming. Vain men are not rare, but a man who well-nigh smothers himself in a cloak of vanity is less common. When Essex forgot to be rude, and forgot to be vain, he was an interesting companion. He would talk freely on all the subjects that interested Gallia, and treat her opinions with the same want of deference he would have shown to a man's. And in all the small ways and manners of life he exercised all the admirable politeness of an ordinary Englishman. It could be seen that the old-fashioned style of woman was his ideal, but Gallia did not quarrel with this, for, sentimentally, the old style of woman was her ideal. 'You cannot,' she would say, 'make yourself the old style of woman; you cannot interfere with the clock of evolution that is wound up and goes on in each one of us; you cannot arbitrarily put back its hands to the time of fifty years ago. Some people's clocks go slower than others, that is all. It isn't that I'm pleased with my pace, or that I like myself as I am, but I'm a quick clock.'

Very often she and Essex found themselves plunging about in

some such arguments. He could not free his mind from the single and only conception of woman of which he was capable, and he looked on what are called, tiresomely enough, new developments in women as fresh forms of wiles, the arts of the nineteenth-century Eve. All this humbugging about at college and wrangling after 'degrees and things' was to him a part of the misguided artfulness of modern women. He couldn't believe in women seriously. Let Gallia talk with her whole soul in her mouth, he would, at his most intolerable, shake his head with a smile – a sort of 'My dear, I see through you' expression, which whipped her up to the point of longing to hit him. This mental attitude of Essex's is very commonly met with, and often in men quite brilliantly clever in their own lines. And the very worst of it is, that they are never to be convinced. One of two things inevitably happens to such men. Either they marry the pretty foolish-kitten style of person, and say triumphantly, 'Of course I was right; just look at Mabel, dear little soul!' when they cannot be contradicted; or the undying womanhood in the woman who burns and argues with them falls a victim to their masculinity, and she spends the rest of her life, after marrying them, in adapting or concealing the parts of her nature which offend the lord god, her husband.

This seems hopeless? Well, it is hopeless. Look at Gallia's case. She didn't know it – that sort of girl never would know it – but she had fallen in love with Essex. She had now left Oxford. There could be no more punting and no more walks. They had met in society, she had been introduced as Lord Hamesthwaite's daughter. Essex had seemed anxious to show her that he could be even ruder to her in that capacity than in her other of simple student; and the upshot of it all was with God and the Fates.

'You will forgive my silence,' he said presently. 'At a dinner one is expected to amuse the lady on one's right, and fill up gaps left by the other man for the lady on one's left, is it not so ? My left appears to have a healthy appetite, and is filling up her own gaps, so we may score her off.'

'Well, then, I claim the amusement due to the lady on your

right,' she exclaimed quickly, and smiled with a touch of girlish pleasure.

'I beg you won't look up at me like that,' Essex said, with a note of protest. 'Have I not told you before that it would upset my whole scheme of life to fall in love with you?'

'And mine.'

'Yours – to fall in love with me?'

'I didn't mean that – and I didn't say it,' Gallia said, with sudden stubbornness.

'Funny; now I consider that you both meant it and said it, but we'll pass that over. Please bear in mind that I am not to be tampered with, that's all. We meet in quite a new fashion; the landscape has changed, the figures in the landscape must change too. We are in London: you on your own ground; I, because Mrs Leighton knew my mother, wanted another man in a hurry, and heard that I had grown up handsome and had a chance of getting disliked into notice some day.'

'Very well. Then you can indulge me with a new form of treatment,' said Gallia, with a nod.

'By the way, the man across there, now gnawing a salt almond, has honoured you with a number of savagely covetous stares.'

'That is Sir Edmund Bruce.'

'It is so delightful to be in the society of some one who is *au fait* with little social details of that kind – to a commoner like myself the greatest treat,' said Essex, with exaggerated enthusiasm.

'You are simply abominable; can you never stop sneering?'

'I breathe again. If you consider me simply abominable, I believe you will not – at least not immediately – fall in love with me! In the meantime, I may tell you that you have improved greatly in doing your hair.'

'Too flattered!' said Gallia, with a curling lip, but she experienced a thrill of gratification all the same.

'Merely justice, I assure you. Have I ever paid you a compliment?'

'One!' she looked up and laughed in his face.

'And that was – ?'

'The compliment of disliking me.'

A shadow came in the middle of Essex's forehead, just between the brows.

'Mr Essex, we are wondering if you can give the explanation of Mark Gurdon's sudden flight to the interior of Africa?' A very pretty little woman, Lady Mary Mortimer, fired this sudden question into the idle bickering Gallia and Essex usually maintained.

'Is it really the interior? When he left, there was word of Cape Town, and since then rumour has pushed him farther and farther towards the tracks of Stanley* and others.'

'Oh, well, it's somewhere in Africa,' Lady Mary explained easily. 'Was it true about his cough?'

'Surely Gurdon didn't mean us to take that seriously ? I had no idea it was intended to go further than his chief.'

'Well, he *had* a cough! Dear Mrs Leighton, you said he had a cough, didn't you?' applying in the most plaintive fashion to her hostess. 'And I have always heard the climate of South Africa was so wonderful for anything of that kind! The air there is so extraordinarily dry, you know.'

'Or so extraordinarily moist, Lady Mary?' Essex interjected gravely.

'Oh yes, I believe that *was* it. Yes, so singularly moist, you know; and of course that is everything in a – in a – bronchial trouble – isn't that what Mr Gurdon had?'

'I can't remember if the cough was in his throat or in his chest,' Mrs Leighton said, with affectionate solicitude.

'I fancy it lay about here,' said Essex, laying a finger in the middle of his brow; 'but I don't think the Colonial Office would mind where it was.'

'You have got to do something for him, Gerald, when he comes home!' Mrs Leighton said warmly. 'Mark Gurdon is a young man I like.'

'His future is assured, Celia.' Lord Hamesthwaite made her a little bow; she kissed the tips of her fingers to him in return.

'He is not to be kept licking envelopes all his young days,' she went on severely. 'And when he comes back from Africa – '

'I wish I knew which part of Africa,' Lady Mary wailed softly.

Lord Hamesthwaite shook his head.

'Ah, I believe he was mistaken in going there,' he said.

'What does he want to endanger his future and his country's future for, by getting to know anything about her dependencies?' Essex said to Gallia, with a little air of irritation which was very well done.

Lord Hamesthwaite looked over quickly to the Oxford man and his daughter, but he did not make any remark.

'Yes; I don't see why he needed to go to Africa,' Mrs Leighton went on.

'His cough,' said Lady Mary tenderly.

'He had just been to Paris too,' her hostess went on, as though this formed an effective reason against a man's going anywhere. 'His French is delicious – quite the French of my own day!'

'Talking of Paris, what news is there of young Robbie?' Lady Hamesthwaite inquired, disengaging herself dexterously from an elderly flirtation with a Dean.

'I very seldom hear from Robbie,' Mrs Leighton replied, with a marked absence of her usual tact, or a conspicuous display of it. Everybody at once felt that Robbie had been 'naughty'.

'My dear,' looking down the table to a very sweet young woman in white, 'have you any news of my grandson to give us?'

'The prettiest girl in the room is blushing; don't miss it,' murmured Essex to his neighbour, and Gallia craned her neck to see who it was he distinguished thus.

'There is very little news to give of an artist before he has arrived,' the prettiest girl said, in a voice of such beauty as made her most ordinary utterance a kind of favour. 'Mr Leighton is to be seen very regularly at the studio – and – that is all! In the spring' – she raised the very glistening grey eyes and swept a glance to Lady Hamesthwaite – 'in the spring, who shall say?'

'You were speaking, Mrs Leighton?' said the courteous peer on her left.

'No, I think not – was I?'

The peer attacked his soufflé with renewed ardour, wondering what the words 'I couldn't have done it better myself' meant. For those words he had certainly overheard.

'Do you really think her so pretty?' Gallia asked, with an elaborate air of criticism.

'She is not only the most beautiful, she is the best woman I have been privileged to know,' Essex replied, with a very new expression, amounting almost to worship, on his face.

It was no wonder if Gallia Hamesthwaite looked up at him in interest and surprise.

The smile with which she was so much more familiar succeeded that new look.

'Don't distress yourself, my dear; she is my sister.'

'Sometimes, you know, Mr Essex – or perhaps you don't know? – your rudeness not only oversteps the bounds of what is permissible – but it ceases to be amusing.'

Gallia turned superbly to the man on her other hand, who chanced to be an old friend.

'Maurice, you are eating far too much pudding! Don't,' she said, with cordial roughness.

'I wondered when you were going to notice me,' the young man replied ruefully, in a very high, thin falsetto voice. 'I have made no less than three distinct remarks to you during dinner, and once I even told you my best story. Not the one about Gladstone and the muffins – that was my best last season – but the one – '

'I expect I know the one,' Gallia remarked coldly.

'No, you can't really; you've been at Oxford all the time! It's the joke they played Rosebery* with his racing-glass. You'll like it awfully. Look here, I'll tell you now, if you'll shunt Essex for a bit.'

'I'm afraid there isn't time; I see Aunt Celia looking at mother. It will keep, won't it?'

'Yes, if you are really – Oh, this is your glove, I expect?' Maurice Forrester was still babbling harmlessly when the ladies left the room.

'Give it to me, I will take it to Miss Hamesthwaite,' Essex said, and said it with so cool an assurance that the glove was meekly handed over to him. A moment later Sir Edmund Bruce dropped into Gallia's vacant chair, and Forrester had to name the men to each other, and observe the neatness with which Essex had got the glove out of sight before Sir Edmund's eye could have fallen on it.

'Let me put it on for you,' Essex said ten minutes later, when he came on Gallia alone in the green gloom of Mrs Leighton's little palm-house. He took her hand in his, turned it over, then spread out the fingers one by one, and folded them together again. Gallia made no sign. She was as though under chloroform, breathing naturally, slightly, her muscles flaccid and limp, her power over herself simply *nil*. Was this the next style of treatment she had asked for?

Essex raised the hand – a white, slim, charming hand it was – a little higher up; he was sitting opposite her on the immense tub of a woolly-stemmed palm. He was going to kiss her hand, she knew; and she knew she was glad that he was going to kiss it: she had one fear which came and went with the throb of her even pulse – that he would put it down without kissing it.

'I wish I were as beautiful as your sister,' Gallia was impelled to say, and she said it with some carelessness and a smile.

'I am glad you are not – or I should worship you,' said Essex, speaking low.

'And if you did?' she asked, looking at him still lightly, and with a curl of amusement on her lips which masked perfectly her curious feelings.

'If I did – I should want you,' he said slowly.

His head was bent and she could not see his face, but she did not care to, she was occupied with her own feelings. Still, it was a strange phenomenon, this Essex with a note of ordinary passion in his voice, a note that Gallia was hearing for the first time in her life. All she knew in the strange confusion of the moment was, that this was not herself, not the old self she had eaten and slept and risen and walked with for so many years. It was a self she had never known or suspected the existence of;

she was sure she would be ashamed of it afterwards – at the time it was too strong for her, and had to have its way and sway. Next, he looked at her, seeming to appraise her, and not unkindly. Few women but have to live through this discomfort, which arises through their having awaked at the wrong moment for the wrong man. 'I should want you,' he had said.

'But my life has no need of you, Gallia, and I don't – I don't.' The head-shake and the sad smile with which he said the last words tore something down in Gallia's soul. The veil of the temple was rent in twain.* It was not that the worst had come, it was that everything had come. There could be nothing any more.

Gallia was in the drawing-room, rallying Maurice about his fund of wit and humour, before that big minute had closed and gone to make up its little hour.

'Never happy any more,'* – where had she heard the line? It was some refrain, apparently, that had stuck in her mind, and she marvelled to hear it beaten out so clearly in the hoof-strokes of her father's horses as they drove home.

Essex sat on the edge of a palm-tub and laughed to himself, and wiped his eyes with a long thin pearl-coloured glove.

Chapter Eight

Five weeks had passed since the dinner at Mrs Leighton's at which Gallia had met Dark Essex, and she had not yet succeeded in comforting herself. Outwardly she had been the same; her way of life was in no wise altered, and at luncheon and dinner, when she joined her father and mother, her dark face sparkled and her sharp young tongue clacked with all their wonted brightness. It was when she got upstairs to her own rooms that the brunt of that meeting made itself felt. She had come to observe narrowly the manner of the recurrence of that recollection – not that this made it any easier to bear, only she was trained to the verbatim reporting of her own feelings, and would not have known how to cease from it. Suppose she was wandering towards her desk, or kneeling on the rug beside her dog, or dislodging the Grand Vizier, as she called her big Persian cat, from his nest among the divan cushions, a blankness would fall upon her mind.

'I remember; there was something that has made me unhappy: what was it?'

Thus her mind would go to work; then suddenly the sharpness of remembrance would lay hold of her nerves, and a little inarticulate cry would escape her; her hands would go up to hide her face, and a shiver, not in her limbs, but in her body, would shake and sicken her. Then with a smile she would say, 'I told him that I loved him, Grand Vizier – no, I asked him to love me – and he pushed me aside like a Piccadilly cab-tout. O God!'

Done with smiling, the shame and the bitterness choked her, and she would bury her face in one of her dozen cushions.

'I used to think no feeling was eternal, or even should be eternal,' she said one day, after some such turn of suffering.

'Life blots out life no less than death does, I used to say to some of the girls. But I was wrong. Some bits of life have a longevity in proportion to their bitterness. Some things one doesn't forget or live out; some feelings have a strength –'

To Gallia, talking aloud was as congenial and familiar as it is to all somewhat separated beings who are in the habit of thinking. She was not, as are many people, self-conscious when left alone with herself, she was at her ease, at home, in the society of someone she at least knew and had tried always to understand.

'I wonder, does the same division obtain in the kingdom of sentiment as obtains in the world? Are there feelings with the life of little animals and birds, and if one strikes them with the will, firmly, do they bleed to death in five minutes; and are there others with the life of the wild beasts in them, that grow stronger and wilder and savager the moment they are wounded, and fight us worse and die hard? Surely the good, kind, sweet feelings are the little animals; how quick charity and good temper and generosity will bleed to death and be forgotten! Passions are the brutes, the lions, tigers, and leopards of that kingdom: they leap up and hit harder and maul worse after the first bullet behind the shoulder. But the reptile feelings – what are they? Slow-lived, poisonous things, that crawl and crawl and drag their wounds with them in no discomfort. Shame is a snake, and you may cut its head off and it will live still. Jealousy, humiliation – the vipers of the feeling world. But shame – shame is a snake, and it is knotted all round me.'

Tears did not come readily to Gallia, but the dry, gasping sort of cries that shuddered through her closed lips every now and then had each the bitterness of many tears.

It was a big, third-floor, three-windowed room looking far into the Green Park that was Gallia's study in the Grosvenor Place house; she had furnished it herself with a keen eye to well-considered shapely spaces of fine flooring. It was not a matter of parquet and prayer-carpets; a wide and wonderful velvet pile in dove-grey and with bouquets of pink and purple flowers in faded tints ran clear to the skirting-board. Upon a dais, so strange a lounge as could never be called a divan had been arranged; a canopy in dull purple and duller gold hung over it, and from a bronze chain a lamp depended, with four purple eyes in its old metal-work, eyes that glowed in the early winter dusk – for Gallia had not switched on her lights yet.

Partly because the room was so wide, partly because the scheme of decoration had been so broadly carried out, Gallia made a very small heap of human suffering kneeling there beside the Grand Vizier, with whose plush existence nothing could ever interfere. Her dark violet cloth gown – so much of herself as not to seem a dress at all – fell sparsely round her, and one meagre purple beam of the little lamp made a violet pool on the cream-coloured nape of her neck.

But Gallia roused herself, and, kneeling and sitting on her heels, looked up towards the light with all the appearance of a young girl before a shrine.

'Why I, with all my interests, should care for any man at all, and that man in particular – I wish I knew if I did really care for him, and I wish I knew what leads him to act, intermittently, as if he cared about me. If I were ever to see him again, I would behave more straightforwardly. I deserved what I got for that vulgar reticence I showed. There is no other word for it. Vulgar; utterly, vilely, customarily, crustedly vulgar. Why couldn't I look up bravely at him? why couldn't I say plainly and simply, "Dark Essex, I love you, do you not love me too?" But no! I am too half-and-half – neither a good woman of the old kind nor a good woman of the new. Surely he would have treated me with respect? No woman – no decent woman – scoffs or jeers at a man who tells her he loves her. If he had not loved me, he could have said so. I would have borne the disappointment with as much pride as I could find, *and I should have been able to respect myself*; there would have been no shame. But what have I done? Let him *play* with me; take my hand and toy with it, and *feel* it, like a hired creature, without even the satisfaction of doing my duty, and fulfilling my part of the bargain, which a hired creature would have had. Lower than the women in the

street I've been; lower than the poor, poor women in the street.
Oh!'

She had come back to the same bitter shudder and the same
sickening sense of degradation. Her head was buried between
her knees now, her white hands squeezed whiter in their
convulsive pressure. Gallia was at the age for what must be
described as 'tall' sentiment. This sort of thing was just as real
to her as would have been any of the real sorrows of life. And
the tiresome part of sorrows is that they do not hurt in
proportion to their validity and excusability. If we are to be
sympathetic, we can remember always that silly suffering hurts
just as much as sensible suffering. A love-trouble, even when
you love the wrong person without having any business to, is
just as bitter as having a relative carried off by a railway
accident.

The soft mumble of the lift-ropes sounded from without, there
was a footstep or two in the passage, the door opened, and the
footman said, 'Mr Essex,' in the strange, hard voice he used
upon the big staircase at parties.

The odious rush of blood in Gallia took from her the power
to think clearly. She knew that, since the door was round a
corner, he would not have seen her; she knew that the room was
almost in darkness; would Hendon turn on the light or not? If
he didn't, and she kept quiet, perhaps Essex would not see. This
jumble of thoughts went through her like a rifle bullet; there
was a little click just before the door closed, and three constellations gleamed out among the wall draperies.

She raised herself softly inside her silken skirt, but the rustle
caught his ear, and he saw – there was no means of disguising it
– that she had been kneeling, that she had been giving way to
emotion, that her self-possession was to seek.

She stood and looked at him for a few moments, saying
nothing, holding out no hand, using the time to collect herself
and decide how to deal with him since he was in her presence.

His smile, his whole air, the way in which he held his hat and
stick, were those of any and every man of manners who makes
a call.

She could read nothing in them.

But she was not like any woman receiving a visitor; there was no reason to battle through the surf of commonplace with Essex before riding upon the deep waters. So she said nothing till he had spoken.

He took no notice of the fashion of his reception; he produced a little package.

'I wanted to return you this myself – because I have been so terribly unfortunate as to burn one page with some cigarette ash,' he said, very easily and well. 'Before replacing the volume with another, which anybody might have done, I wanted to show it you and ask you to let me mend it. You see, I thought, as there are some marks in it, you might value this copy. Now, it *can* be mended by means of this other copy I bring. Dear Miss Hamesthwaite, what is the matter with you? you are not suffering from a stiff neck, I hope?'

In spite of herself Gallia laughed.

'I believe that is it,' she said drily.

'Well, I daresay you are not in the mood for visitors, but give me your attention for three minutes, and then I will go.'

This alarmed her very much indeed: unprepared for his coming, she was less prepared to have him go. But she said no word till they had opened the little book and discussed its wound. She would have nothing done to it; she knew the word that was missing in the verse, and it might have been her own cigarette any day in the week. She forgave it freely.

'Since you are so good, I will go.'

'Since I am so good, I think you might stay. I want to ask you something. Sit down somewhere.'

He took a chair, put his hat and stick upon the floor, and leaned towards her with his hands – very fine sallow hands – dangling between his knees. It was an attitude of uncompromising attention. For the moment Gallia was unnerved. She altered her plan of attack.

'Why are you so different today?' she said, in a manner very natural and frank.

'That cannot have been what you wanted to ask me, but I will answer it if you wish. This is my afternoon manner; I put it on with this coat.' He glanced down the front of himself, and dusted a slight speck from its lodgment between two buttons. As he sat there, he was an infinitely elegant and correct presentment of a man of his world. Gallia wondered how he could conceal so much divergence from the type inside one frock-coat.

'I am going to ask you to let me refer to our last meeting,' she said gently and very gravely, 'or rather parting.'

'You got up and rushed off, if I remember.'

Gallia believed he was nervous underneath his smile.

'I greatly regret my manner all through that interview – it was not sufficiently frank or straightforward.'

He looked genuinely surprised.

'I don't know if you will agree with my summary of the interview, so I will put a question to you first. Will you really say what you think in reply?'

'No, I can't make any such promise.'

'But you will try to answer truly?'

'If I can, I will.'

'What did you think were my feelings for you that evening – particularly during the time we sat in the palm-house?'

'I am glad to be able to speak by the book. You thought me "simply abominable".'

'Ah, no, don't joke – that is only another complication. But if jokes are to count,' with a feminine whisk of her tactics, 'did you think I was really in danger of doing so when you asked me not to fall in love with you?'

'Every woman is – are we to say in danger? – very well – is in danger of falling in love, as they have agreed to term it, with every man when the people in question are your and my ages, and have corresponding appearances and gifts.'

'Is every man in danger of falling in love with every woman, then – given the same conditions as you name?'

'Certainly.'

'Well, did you think then – do you think now – that I have fallen in love with you?'

'How could I be so vain as to say so, if I did think it?'

'I perceive that I have begun ill – you are not replying well. We must do it some other way. I am going to grant that my manner in the palm-house could readily have given you the impression that I was in love with you.'

'If it did, if you were, if I was, if neither of us is – what matter, so long as we say nothing about it to each other?'

'I can't agree with you there.'

'Of course not, because you are a woman, and must continually be pulling up a plant to see how it is growing. Now, for Heaven's sake, don't snatch at that wretched metaphor and turn it some other way on!'

'I am going to do nothing of the kind.'

She got up from her chair some yard or two away, came up to him and put her hands on his shoulders; as he didn't look up, she raised his chin with one stiff finger. Her eyes had a different kind of light, her lips were parted, and her voice, when it came, was rich, tender, beautiful as he had never heard it.

'Listen! I owe you a straight speech, and even if you don't want to hear it, bear with me, for it hurts so to know one has not been true to oneself – that one hasn't had *courage*. Oh, there isn't anything women want except courage – they have to use so much, much more than men. If I spend all mine in the next minute, it will be good; I shall have been true. The other night, I don't know what took hold of me; I have felt once or twice that you were different from any other man I've seen, and made me feel different. I think, in a crowd, if you had been somewhere behind me, I'd have known you were there. The other night, though you said one rude thing after another, and didn't use even the commonest civility to me, my whole soul wrapped itself up in one thought; it seemed to sit with folded arms inside me, waiting for you, wanting you to kiss my hand. I didn't know it then, but I believe now that that means that I love you. Hush! – wait. It is all right – I know you said it – your life has no need of me, and I am not beautiful enough for you to worship – that on one side. You have no need of me. I don't think you told me as kindly as you might. One never knows, but I think – well,

yes, I think if it had been *you* showing *me* that you loved me,
and if I had felt like you – I think I would have spoken
differently! But, however, it came! I am young, and I can put up
with it. I have loved you – it is right that you should know it; I
love you still, and may do so for a long time; but I want you to
forgive me for the other evening. It was immodest, flagrant,
shameless, the way I sat there and said nothing, and let you use
me as you did. That was disgraceful, and though I have tried, I
can't forget the shame of it. But it was so new to me then, I was
taken by surprise. I had not an idea that I loved you, or I would
have been ready to speak. I would have said, "No, none of these
simulacra with me; I really love you, and they insult me." But I
will forget those to you, for perhaps you *did* not guess I loved
you. Will you try to forgive me my want of honesty, since I have
tried to make up for it now?'

Chapter Nine

She stood back from him, her arms at her sides, waiting, as though for a sentence, for his reply. He got up and went over to lean upon the mantelshelf. With an elbow in one of its dusky oak crevices, and his face finely thrown up by the background of carving, he was still at his full height, and he felt free, his own man.

For a moment, as she watched him keenly, Gallia thought he was going to be natural, to be what she knew he might be if ever he would give his inner self free play; but next instant a smile rose, and her head rolled from side to side in the impatience she immediately felt of the manner he was assuming.

'It has been a question in good society,' he began very slowly, 'how far it is justifiable for one person to place another person in an impossible position; you will, since you are a member of that society, know doubtless better than I do how this question has been decided. But out of the depths of a somewhat sickly experience of the world, I am able to tell you one thing – that, had you said these things to nine out of ten other men, they would have seized and kissed you, and said God knows what, that you wouldn't have been prepared to hear. And they would have been in no sense to blame. You are going to say that they would not have been gentlemen.'

'I wasn't; I was going to say they could hardly be so dull of apprehension as to so mistake me,' cried Gallia hotly.

'It would not have been a matter of apprehension, dull or the reverse. It would have been a matter of convention. Men are always expected, in certain positions, to show passion.' He smiled very drily. 'They are expected – by women at least – to be what women call *men*. Nine out of ten women would have meant that speech to end in a smother of embraces. One moment. I am not in the least certain that you are the tenth woman, I am only sure that I am the tenth man. You will admit that I have not kissed you?'

'Why should I mind if you had, when I love you?' Gallia asked simply. 'You know I didn't *mean* things to end in one way or another. I said what I thought I ought to say to save my own self-respect, and you were and are free to act exactly as you think right or feel inclined. Though I would, of course, prefer you to understand rather than misunderstand me.'

A footman came in at this moment.

'Her ladyship wished me to say Mr Gurdon was in the drawing-room, and if you were disengaged, she would like you to come down, miss.'

'Say to her ladyship, Hendon, that I am not able to come down this afternoon.'

He went out, and Gallia turned to Essex again.

'Why can you not treat me with the same decency a woman is expected to show a man when he tells her he loves her? What is the difference?'

'I daresay from your point of view there is no difference, and I hope you will think that I have behaved myself as becomingly as any woman could have done.'

'Well, you have not acted like the nine men you mention, from one of two reasons. Perhaps because you had the sense to see that I expected nothing of the kind, perhaps because you did not happen to have the feelings you say they would have had.'

'I am not in the least moved to explain which,' said Essex calmly. 'The subject of what you and a number of other people call love may be one I have never studied, or it may be that I have read further into it than you have done. Perhaps I call love by some other names, perhaps I don't even see it to be a fine and desirable feeling. We needn't go into that.'

'No, we needn't; there is no question of it. I had merely to explain conduct I was ashamed of, to explain it for my own sake; I have done. I am glad and proud again; I have not, if you have understood me, anything more to feel ashamed of.' She came up to him and took his hand. 'Thank you. You at any rate listened to me – I am grateful for it.'

If ever a pair of sincere eyes looked up at a man, they were Gallia's. Essex, even through his priggishness and affectation, was conscious of being at a disadvantage.

'By the way,' with a complete change of tone, 'you had a glove of mine – will you please give it me?'

'Are you afraid I may make a trophy of it?'

She shook her head and smiled a little wistfully.

'No, you won't make me believe you really credit me with so unworthy a thought.'

'I haven't it with me now; I will post it to you.'

'Thanks.'

'And – don't you think the world is still a little too raw for your very advanced treatment of it?'

He went to get his hat and stick.

'No,' said Gallia firmly, and sitting down among her cushions; 'the world is never too raw for a woman to do what she thinks right. She would help to keep it raw by playing down to its rawness. There can be no excuse for not acting in accordance with the light one has. One may be misunderstood, one may be disliked, but we have to save our own souls for ourselves.'

'And the dramatic faculty inherent in all women makes the saving process so much the more picturesque.'

A disheartened note of sad laughter came from her.

'Goodbye,' was all she said.

'If one could believe you sincere, you would be worth loving, by some better man than I. Goodbye, O New Woman, who is yet the old!'

'Goodbye, epitome of unbelief.' Gallia was smiling too. 'If only you have not put out my soul's little light!'* she added, half to herself, in a frightened whisper.

This time Essex laughed musically as he went to the door.

'Let me know if I have,' were the last words she heard him say; then the door shut, the lift-ropes rumbled again, and two minutes later she watched him cross the road towards the Park gates.

She drew a nervous breath or two, and passed her handker-chief below the curls on her forhead.

'That is the end of that,' she said. 'If I had foreseen his coming at all, I should have foreseen his going too. It is no worse and no better than I might have imagined it.' She walked up and down the big room several times, not so much thinking as struggling to get hold of her feelings, and know what she thought.

'Life is no different now from what it was,' she told herself, 'and yet I feel as though I had to gather up the threads and see into what kind of knot I can tie them, and how I can get them to hold. Nothing has really happened, only now I know that something is not going to happen – for instance, love is not going to happen. What did he mean about the name he might call it by? Of course he must see it very differently from me. He hinted that he thought it neither fine nor desirable. That was very honest of him. I was too hard; I didn't think – one never does think till afterwards – that of course he cannot respect love. What man can be honest with himself and about himself? I wish I had told him that I saw that, that I knew that! And I wish – oh, how I wish I had asked him to kiss me once! Perhaps he would have said no; but if he would have consented to be simple, surely he would not have minded kissing me just once! A woman always grants as much as that, and shines in doing it. It is looked on as a sacrifice on her part, and no one thinks the worse of her. Could anyone, even himself, have thought the worse of him? Ah, how I wish – I wish' – a rush of emotion almost choked her, but she flung her head up and ran to the window to look at the lights twinkling across the Park; with her hands clinging to the casement bar, she leaned there a moment. 'For now I shall never be kissed, and it cannot be good *never* to have been kissed at all! Well, there will be one of the flowers of life I shall never have picked – a love-kiss. Surely, surely no woman can be so mean and poor a creature as not to be worth and worthy of one man's kiss?'

Her earnestness was pitiful. Essex had fatuously mistaken Gallia: she had absolutely no dramatic faculty, was never conscious of her attitude or her expression, or the strength of the feeling from an outside point of view. She was only bitterly and clearly honest in herself and to others; her ideal was high, and her ideal was absolute reality. She had never buried any truth from herself, and could not easily understand the desire to do so which is so common. In spite of a very wideawake mind, she had no idea to what extent compromise enters into the most honourable man's idea of honour. As a woman, she took honour and honesty very seriously, well knowing them to be among the latest branches of study opened to her sex, and deeply sensible of their importance; but of the necessity for compromise even in such holy of holies she knew nothing.

Entirely without conceit and self-consciousness, her whole life was a desire to know, and then to be true to what she knew. Crude and perhaps ludicrous as she might now and then appear, her single-mindedness was her most marked characteristic. Had she been different, had she had the skill of any of the nine women Essex had cited, she would have been nine times better fitted to win his love – only she would never have striven to do it.

She suffered at this time because her views were nobler, she herself a little better than common; such human creatures as differ thus from their fellows are rarely made welcome in the world of men and women in which she lived.

It was so late now that she hurried to her rooms. There were no tears to dry, no eyes that needed bathing, no sign for a maid's keen eyes to notice that her mistress had lived through any scene. When she came running from her bath, she brought a calm, quiet face with her, and immersed herself quite naturally in the evening papers while her hair was being dressed. Her mother was in the drawing-room, with a magazine and a paper-cutter, as usual, when she went in; they were to dine alone, and to pick Lord Hamesthwaite up at eleven at the House on their way to a reception.

'So sorry, dear, that you could not come down when Mark Gurdon was here; he was so interesting about Africa,' Lady

Hamesthwaite said pleasantly, with her customary proud smile at her daughter's beautiful face.

'Mr Essex came in, and I really think he must have stayed two hours with me,' Gallia replied, naturally.

Do you like Mr Essex very much?'

Gallia paused to weigh her words.

'No, mother; I don't think I like him particularly at all.'

'Who is Essex, by the way?' Lord Hamesthwaite had come in and overheard these remarks.

'He is an Oxford man; a Fellow and a tutor. He writes a good deal for the literary weeklies, I think,' Gallia answered; 'and he is often in London, for his mother is a great invalid. They have a house – in Hammersmith Terrace, I believe he said – and they are very poor.'

'His sister is a very beautiful woman,' said Gallia's father judicially.

'Yes; I would like to know her so much.'

'You are sure to meet her at Aunt Celia's; she is a great pet there.'

They rose to pass in to dinner.

A handsome family, then,' Lord Hamesthwaite said; 'that young man had a very unusual type of good looks, but I am afraid he is a prig.'

Gallia was not at a point whence she could perceive the rugged truth of this dictum. Besides, she would have persisted in loving him even had she been convinced of his prighood. He was the first man she had loved, and the first man is never a woman's free choice. Like the first fish of the amateur trouter, he is an accident; neither science, skill, nor selection has a hand in landing him. Sometimes he is a handsome and creditable accident. I have known the first man in more than one case to be a meritorious person – oftenest, though, he is a very mean, small-finned little accident.

The conversation drifted off to Mark Gurdon again and his African experiences.

'I believe he is to be at Axminster's dinner at the Reform*

tomorrow; I must keep my eye on him if Celia wants him helped into something.'

Nothing seemed more natural to Lord Hamesthwaite than that a young man should want to be helped into something; whereas to hear that a man wrote for literary weeklies was to hear something that made it very difficult to realise his personality.

'Poor old Mr Quittenden has had another stroke,' Gallia remarked presently, feeling within herself a strong need of the relief of the commonplace. And someone else's tragedy is just as often our commonplace as our tragedy is theirs.

'Where did you see that ?' Lord Hamesthwaite asked quickly.

'All the papers have the telegram.'

'This child may be trusted,' Lady Hamesthwaite began laughingly, 'to see and know of what is happening' – She was interrupted by a fit of coughing; her husband looked quickly up at her, but said nothing.

'Ah, that was the second stroke, wasn't it? It can only be a matter of weeks – or, at most, months – for the member for Hollowhampton.'

'Poor old thing! I liked him so much that one day he lunched here,' Gallia said. 'It is really very sad.'

''m, yes!' replied her father, who keenly remembered Mr Quittenden's action regarding a certain Bill, and wasn't so sure that it would be so very sad for his party.

'He was always such an admirer of yours, Gerald!'

Lord Hamesthwaite looked doubtfully at his wife.

'I remember so well his saying to me, "There isn't another man in England who so completely fills the idea of a" – ' Again Lady Hamesthwaite was interrupted by the same strange, choking cough.

'Now, Julia,' Lord Hamesthwaite burst out, bringing his fingers sharply on the table, 'this settles it. London is not for you. Don't say a word – I will have my own way about it. Gallia, your mother must go abroad at once. I've been very patient. I've watched this getting worse daily, and I've seen the futility of treatment. No doubt I've been a fool to hold my tongue so long about it. But go she must, and that immediately.'

'But my dinners, my receptions – the invitations are all out!' poor Lady Hamesthwaite interjected pathetically. 'And Gallia, whom I thought I was to have the happiness of taking about with me this year –'

'Gallia will go with you, as I cannot leave town. She has finished with Oxford. You can take her, or she can take you, about the Riviera, if you like.'

Gallia had one moment of communing with herself, then she said cheerfully, 'I'll tell you where we'll go, mother, we will go to Algiers. It will do you heaps of good.'

And so they spent most of the evening discussing and forming plans.

The last post brought Gallia a small registered package. Within it was one long glove and one of Mr Essex's cards.

She turned them over several times, amused at the over-care, in which she detected more than a spice of scorn, which had registered the tiny parcel, hurt somehow by the formality of the visiting card. She turned over the doubled sheet of notepaper and looked inside the envelope. There was no word, not a penscratch. Just the address in Essex's little cramped Greek handwriting.*

'Yes, mother, let it be Algiers. And – let us go tomorrow. We can spend a week in Cannes to get anything you may need.'

'My dear, I need nothing but what can be telegraphed for to Paris; but tomorrow –'

'*Do* let it be tomorrow, if you can, dear. I am so sick of – I hate – hate – hate this place so!' She flung herself back in her chair so violently, and threw her arms above her head with so much vehemence, that the little matters on her knees, the glove and its belongings, fell upon the floor. Lady Hamesthwaite noticed them with her kind, tactful eyes, and came over to Gallia and kissed her.

'Tomorrow or next day, dear, at latest. Now, away to bed; we shall be so busy all day seeing people, and explaining things, and writing notes.'

Chapter Ten

Mrs Leighton happened to be giving a little luncheon party, when Lady Hamesthwaite ran in on the following morning to announce the Algiers programme, and find condolence for the necessity of giving up all her social ploys for the winter. Margaret Essex, whom Mrs Leighton frankly delighted in because she was so beautiful, and Mark Gurdon were of the party, and they sat next each other.

Every man has, at the bottom of his heart, an admiration, more or less strong according to his temperament, for the delicately beautiful, beneficent-faced, and gracious married woman – the woman of the kind eyes and tender mouth. It is less the beauty of this sort of woman than her beneficent air that wins him. She is the woman who draws most souls to follow after her, she has the face which could start a crusade. She may have moments that are humanly pranksome, but she is guileless-ness itself. She is more wonderful at thirty than at twenty, for the persistent beauty of her character, as it grows stronger and stronger, can draw only beautiful lines in her face. We may thank our stars and gods that hers is an inextinguishable race, that there will always be some of these women to be found, that where they walk, things hopelessly wicked will bud out into goodness, and good things be better. We can only have one quarrel against them; that their immemorial fine forgiveness may perpetuate things indifferently good and bad.

Margaret Essex was young yet, but the mark belonging to this race of souls was set on her forehead already. She was not very clever, she had not much brain, and her training had been desultory; but none of those things matter in such a woman. I think she may be exempted from tediously practical formulæ, and the set duties of a dull world; in the advancement of women she must always be franked. On the whole, it is admitted by right that woman's sense of law, order, and judgment should be taught as they are being taught now; but this must not apply to the soul-woman I am speaking of. She has a track of her own to follow, lonely and lovely. She is amenable to laws as mysterious to us as those that tell the tides when to turn.

Enough of her. This was the race to which Margaret Essex belonged, and Gurdon had summed her up coldly and foolishly on that day when she passed him by in Paris. He knew now that he had been wrong. He had never talked to any woman in his life who gave him the same feelings as this one. Man is approached through his simple senses first; a goddess may sit at his elbow, and the turn of her wrist as she handles a fork will be the first of her charms to arouse his regards. Mark found himself watching Margaret's fingers as she crumbled her bread, and wondering if it were merely that he had never observed women's fingers before, or if hers were really so infinitely more delicate in colouring and contour than those of any other woman? They were flower-fingers. Then her voice, her habit of speaking with her eyes cast down in thought, and at the end of her sentence, or if she put a question, raising them with so clear and direct a glance; this unconscious charm he caught himself waiting for, with an eagerness that was utterly foreign to his whole nature as he knew it. That she had not recognised him as the man who had been walking that day in the Jardin du Luxembourg with Leighton was quite certain; so far she had only heard of him as being newly returned from Africa, and he had carefully refrained from mentioning Paris. Strange, but he would have been unanxious for her to identify him as Leighton's friend at this early moment of their acquaintance. She disapproved of Leighton. She must have learned – she couldn't have failed to learn – of Leighton's relations with Arsénie, and Gurdon didn't find it anything but natural that her favour was removed from a man who openly kept a mistress. Gurdon was a man of no imagination whatever; for him, what was, was. It was habitual for women to disapprove of a man who kept a mistress and took small pains to conceal this fact; just as it was habitual for them to receive intimately, and finally marry, men who had connections, decently regulated and properly concealed, of a more casual nature. Gurdon hadn't a shadow of doubt in his mind that Margaret's moral views were of this complicated but no less universal pattern; he felt sure she would recognise the same difference between the two kinds of men that he did; and he sympathised with her in the shock she must have experienced in discovering Leighton's lapse from this high standard, and felt that she was entirely justified in dropping his acquaintance. There was one little faint distinction, which he would have admitted, but which did not happen to occur to him. He would have excused Leighton everything but the publicity of his behaviour; and Margaret would not. But this was, after all, a very, very faint distinction, although in the present case it had been the direct cause of Leighton's losing her friendship.

Margaret had been what may be described as 'carefully brought up'; she had lost her father early, but her mother, who was a clever and a charming woman, had herself accompanied her to Germany, and then to France, for educational purposes; and it was only during the last year, when Mrs Essex had become too much of an invalid to leave her home, that she had consented unwillingly to her daughter's studying art in Paris. So far as it could be, everything that could be done was done, and every precaution taken; with the result that Margaret's sojourn gained greatly in dullness and propriety, while it certainly lost in gaiety and charm. The five hundred a year which was Mrs Essex's income amply sufficed to keep going the little house in Hammersmith Terrace, and Essex, though he was not particularly generous, provided his sister's dress allowance from his own not over well-filled coffers.

They were the widow's only children, and though the son had her own dark kind of beauty (so much so, that his real name, Hubert, had fallen into disuse, and most people spoke of him as Dark, a sobriquet he had acquired at Winchester), it was on Margaret's face, the fair refinement of her dead husband's, that Mrs Essex loved best to look.

'Do you know, I haven't seen your brother for years, and

once I was very much indebted to him down at Oxford,' Gurdon said, gliding carefully away from the subject of art, which was too nearly allied to Paris to be safe for discussion.

'What did he do for you?' Margaret asked.

'Oh, he read with me; gave me a short cut when I had been neglecting my reading badly, and was becoming scared at the thought of the exams.'

'He can't be much older than you?'

'No; but he had had the benefit of a consistent classical education, and was years ahead of me in most things,' Gurdon answered; and was amused to find a man of his experience speaking of a consistent classical education as a benefit.

'He is fearfully clever,' Margaret said, betraying a simple worship, which Gurdon thought as delightful as it is nowadays proportionately rare. Though he did not know many women, Gurdon was dimly aware that they were no longer in the habit of thinking men 'fearfully clever'; he knew that some totally different spirit was abroad. How refreshing to come across a beautiful woman, a woman of spirit too, like Margaret Essex, who was still able to look up in worship of the man she thought fearfully clever!

'Would he be likely to be at home if I were to call some day a little after five?' Gurdon said, rather disingenuously, and meaning 'Would you be at home?'

'He goes down to Oxford tomorrow. What a pity!' The eyes rested on him again, with their frank, glistening look. 'He is at home today, going over his books.'

'If it would be convenient, I might drive down today. It is Hammersmith, is it not?' Gurdon did not ask himself why he was so anxious to get a footing in that Hammersmith house – time enough for reflection afterwards; but he knew very well what he wanted, and he saw proudly that he had secured it.

Luncheon was over at last, and guests left early, as everybody knew that Lady Hamesthwaite had come for a last interview with her sister; and a few people who had heard her cough, and who felt that easy lack of responsibility in disposing of their friends which is so common, thought that it might indeed prove to be her last interview.

'You will let me see you to the train?' Gurdon was saying to Margaret in the hall, as she stood fastening her little sable close round her neck.

'Thank you, but I am going to walk up Gloucester Road and take an omnibus; the train is nearer and quicker, of course, but we don't often have so bright an afternoon as this.'

'Then perhaps I may see you to the omnibus? 'Mark said, with a smile.

'If it is your way.'

'Did you not tell me I could find your brother this afternoon?'

'Oh, you are coming out too?' She did not seem to have grasped this, and she turned to him with a little sparkle of surprise.

'However innocent a woman may be, it is safer not to presume too much upon that innocence,' thought the cautious Mark very wisely. A sun of shrewdness and womanly intuition is apt to break through those poetic blue mists of unsuspicion.

'It would be a pleasure to me to see him again; and this seems to be my only chance,' he replied coolly.

A few moments later they had scaled the stairway of a red 'road-car',* and settled themselves easily and simply in the close quarters of a garden-seat.

'For real exhilaration, give me the top of an omnibus on a fine afternoon in London,' Margaret exclaimed, with evident enjoyment, as they rolled quickly over the good wood pavement.* 'The men drive so splendidly, and it seems to me an omnibus always gets through things before every other conveyance. I love to feel the on and off of the brake, and to watch the way the pole* seems to feel its way through the traffic. The lightness and balance of these poles must be wonderful, you know – a touch sways them. Then the horses are so nice and fat and strong, and you never see a lame horse in an omnibus, whereas nearly *all* the horses in cabs have something the matter with them.'

'I confess these things never struck me before, but you are

perfectly right,' Mark said, feeling a genuine interest for the moment in noticing the points she referred to.

'Oh, without its omnibuses London would lose half its charm for me.'

'Do you know, your power of observation must be very keen indeed? Of course, that is what makes you an artist.'

'Oh no! You are quite wrong – really you are! The observation that detects shades of lameness in cab-horses is not a bit the sort an artist ought to have. And that happens to be one of my great difficulties. I am far too careful of detail. "*Cherchez le mouvement*," one of the professors says to me twice a week. "*Mais, mademoiselle, il faut cligner les yeux.*"*

'Well, but surely –'

'Yes; but he doesn't mean the peculiarities of movement in a cab-horse,' said Margaret, laughing; 'it is the effect I have to search for, and the central principle movement. I can't explain it at all – I never could explain anything – but you know that an artist has to look at effects through half-closed eyes; if you are to be broad, if you are to get your planes of colour right and your values, you mustn't go darting weasel-gimlet glances here and there for little minor details.'

'You have cleared up the whole matter for me in a phrase. "Weasel-gimlet glances" is excellent. I never thought of this before, but I see there are many distinctions even among good powers of observation. My own are fairly good, and they are neither like yours nor those you want to acquire. My eyes seem to have little independence. I can walk a mile and see nothing, but if I bring my head into play, my eyes will register with a photographic accuracy, and I have complete pictures of places, people, and things fixed firmly on the retina of my brain – which I would swear by in a court of law afterwards, if need were.'

Margaret looked at him critically, listened carefully, and then said, with a very ingenuous touch of admiration, 'That is a splendid power to have at command. I expect you have trained it greatly?'

'I have tried to strengthen it, I think. But,' smilingly, 'I have never tried to talk of it before, and you must look kindly on my egotism for once.'

She had no need to reply except with a smile, for they were at Hammersmith, and obliged to clamber carefully down. The way Margaret swung the tails of her skirt round her, and positively ran down the stair, while every other woman blundered into more or less of an exposure of boot-top, thick, shapeless leg, and repellent underskirt, was another point which Gurdon registered politely in Margaret's favour.

'We have a little walk now,' she said, and they set off down the bustling, horrible King Street, having continually to avoid the footpath on account of the crowds at the doors of multifarious gin-shops.

It was not a moment for conversation, and Gurdon was busy wondering how he was to account to Essex himself for the enthusiasm which had brought him down. If he remembered, Essex was a silent, severe, satirical person, who would be quite keen enough to see through the object of Mark's visit, and who would further be quite cool enough not to help him to carry off the situation with *éclat*. The two men had never actually been friends, though they had known each other very well and met very frequently; and though, as Gurdon had said, Essex had helped him materially when reading for his degree, yet they had never passed that indefinable barrier between knowing one another well and being friends.

But small difficulties only whetted Mark's courage, and he followed Margaret into the drawing-room with a good air of self-possession.

Chapter Eleven

As a matter of fact, that call in Hammersmith turned out exceedingly well. It is only necessary to go to a place in sufficient trepidation, and a visit always will turn out well, provided the trepidation does not bereave the caller of his senses. Gurdon's trepidation did not so bereave him; he was only conscious of having padded out a college intimacy slightly, and this for his own excellent purposes. Once inside the house, he had a quarter of an hour in which to get on terms with Mrs Essex; this was the kind of social enterprise in which success was certain to him. Mrs Essex brought out her best conversation, and imagined that she had been entertaining a young man of public importance, as well as a young man whom Margaret must like, or else why had she brought him down – upon an omnibus, too, that very hob-nobby and familiar vehicle? Her son, coming into the room and finding them talking and laughing with such freedom and good understanding, himself being a remarkably self-centred person, accepted Gurdon as his sister's and his mother's friend, remembered him as a very decent fellow when he was 'up', and chimed in agreeably in the mutual harmony of the moment.

Mark left, feeling that Essex was improved since college days; that he was more a man of the world and more human. 'I remember, I believe, that I liked Essex very well,' he said to himself as he went westwards in a train; and certainly Gurdon was not the man to notice the amazing narrowness of mind which was one of Essex's worst faults, and which the life open to a Fellow of an exclusive college does nothing to minimise.

During the long, wintry spring the two men met a number of times. When Essex was in town, he dined at the club with Mark; and once, when a big statesman went down to speak at Oxford, Gurdon was Essex's guest for a couple of days.

But before they encountered one another again at the house in Hammersmith, Mark had established a habit of going to supper there on Sunday evenings; and it was an odd week when he did not manage to see Margaret somewhere, at least once, in between times.

The fact was, that he was desperately attracted towards her, and when in her presence did not recognise himself for the same man: his nature seemed changed; he expressed opinions with unimpeachable sincerity, which were in direct opposition to the opinions he would have expressed to the men he was in the habit of dining and talking with at the club. He couldn't fail to notice the extraordinary effect the girl had on him. Sometimes he knew he was in love with her; he knew that he was going to ask her to marry him if he had any sort of chance to do so; he knew that he would be ruthlessly cutting up his schemes for his own life and future, and he knew he would be acting like a fool. At least, he knew these things when he got back to his own *milieu*; he did not know them at Hammersmith, and he did not know them in the train; – the train formed a kind of hot, yeasty interlude, when he sat still and read his papers with difficulty, feeling all the time a restlessness and a desire to gaze into space with a smile upon his face which must have betrayed his errand to the stockbroker opposite.

At his rooms, in the big leather armchair which had been his father's, and which had faithfully hatched out schemes of transcendent ambition in all his years of office life, Mark had terrible hours. He was a traitor to these schemes at heart. He was a traitor to that chair. One part of his brain looked on in a sort of cold horror, while the other part sketched out a future which should be more successful because of the lovely wife who would share it. 'It all depends on *whom* a man marries,' he would say didactically to himself, well knowing that it does not. A woman with a great deal of money would not have retarded him; any other woman, no matter how clever and beautiful and distinguished, certainly would; Mark knew, as well as any man in Whitehall, that the day is past when women could play a part in the diplomatic world by reason of personal talent or beauty.

Money, and money only, and a great deal of money at that, would have helped him. He was an exceptionally clear-eyed person; he had studied all the possibilities of advancement in parliamentary and diplomatic circles; also he had looked round him. He could, with the help of a rich wife, buy a capital position as a junior politician. But Margaret was poor. Double and treble milled was each one of these thoughts, yet, once at Hammersmith and in the room, they left him. He was at his ease and natural again; natural with the nature Margaret had called up in him.

Both mother and daughter thought him 'delightful', and very clever and full of power and determination. They magnified his good qualities, as kind women will, and they never observed his bad qualities at all; for which they are not to be blamed, as these were very negative in Mark, and might almost be said to be non-existent at that time. However innocent Margaret may have been of the construction which might be put upon Mr Gurdon's visits, and the meaning he managed to throw into them – and it is permissible to imagine Margaret just as innocent as a 'nice' girl ought to be – it was not to be supposed that their intention escaped Mrs Essex. She saw perfectly well, with matronly clearness, in fact, that 'young Mr Gurdon was interested in dear Margaret', had, in fact, fallen in love with her.

'I suppose we shall have Mr Gurdon as usual about seven o'clock,' she said, smiling indulgently, as she prepared to snatch a few moments' sleep in her armchair after tea.

'I daresay,' Margaret answered from the piano, and without interrupting the 'Schlummerlied'* she was softly playing.

'I like to see a determined lover,' Mrs Essex went on, still with the same complacence. The 'Schlummerlied' came to an end.

'A determined *what*?'

'My dear child, of course you are aware that he may propose any day?' Mrs Essex roused herself a little at Margaret's tone, and a moment or two later she saw that her sleep that afternoon must be given up.

'It is a little hard that every intimacy with a man may have to be terminated just at the comfortable point – because he thinks it necessary to propose,' Margaret said, with a sense of injury, but an air of great self-possession. 'Not that I have seen any signs of his forgetting himself in that way,' she added, smiling.

'You may be perfectly assured that he is going to propose to you. He has singled you out, ever since he came here, by the most marked attention. He has sent you books and songs; he has brought you flowers; he has come early – and – and – not gone away till very late; and he never takes his eyes off you when he is in the room.'

Mrs Essex enumerated these points in a helpless tone, and Margaret nodded, and ticked each one on her slim fingers. Very true – what can a man do more?

'In fact, he has shown all the polite signs of being in love,' she said, laughing, and looking very pretty. Any girl will laugh and look pretty when she hears of the subjection of a presentable victim; she is only haughty and insulted if the victim is not presentable. Her own feelings for the man do not come into the question at all at this stage. 'Well,' she went on, still smiling, and still looking pretty, 'we will exhibit all the polite signs in the reverse direction. As I am not going to accept him, and shouldn't think of doing so, we must begin at once. For instance: I will have a headache, and be lying down upstairs when he arrives. You will entertain him till supper-time. I will struggle down to supper, looking very pale.'

'That of course will bring matters to a head immediately,' Mrs Essex broke in, and herself unable to prevent a smile at Margaret's nonsense.

'Oh, but I won't be lackadaisical and floppy. My headache will be of the severe kind, and my manner will be as severe as the headache. You, in the meantime, will have prepared the way by talking about other men I have known and liked. I think, you know, one gets through these things quicker and more painlessly if one conducts them on the "someone else" tack; a man will go away if he is made to understand that there is another man, but he won't if he thinks you are fancy-free. Well, he hardly could – it would be rude of him. He has to stay and teach you to care

for him. I owe these ideas entirely to novels, but novelists make
a study of such points. So you will tell him about other men.'

'But what other men? I don't at this moment know of any
other men. You see, Margaret, you have not been like most girls
of the present day; you have not had batches of "men friends".'

Margaret nodded. 'I've had a mother-friend,' she said.

'Now, let me think whom you have known. But, in any case,
it would not be honourable or true of us to mix up any man's
name with yours – merely to put off Mr Gurdon. I should not
at all like it.'

'Dear mamma, you take it too seriously; you haven't to say
anything at all. After all, I'm quite as likely to marry any of the
men I've known as Gurdon.'

'Mr Gurdon, dear; don't get into the habit of speaking of men
by their surnames – even to me. It is very fast, I think.'

'Not exactly fast, now, mamma, surely, though it may have
been once. I expect I have caught the habit among the girls in
Paris. They do it, but not from fastness, merely from economy
of time.'

'It occurs to me that the only young man you have known is
Mr Robert Leighton.' The word 'Paris' had obviously suggested
him to her mother, and Margaret, who was standing over by a
window that looked upon the river, felt suddenly frightened.

'I wouldn't mention his name, mamma. In fact, I agree with
you that perhaps it wouldn't be at all a good plan to do as I
said.'

'The best thing for you to do is to tell him firmly and quietly
that you don't, and never can, care for him – if that is the case.'
Mrs Essex sighed – from mixed motives, for she had never been
able to contemplate the idea of Margaret's marriage with
equanimity, and it was also true that she had had pangs of sheer
jealousy when she had seen Gurdon and the girl laughing and
chatting in a certain youthful intimacy that she of course could
never have with her daughter; at the same time, as a woman,
she had to be sorry for a lover.

'I will not have a headache at all, on second thoughts,'
Margaret announced presently.

'Well, then, I think I will,' Mrs Essex said lightly, and rising from a chair. 'The room is very warm, Margaret, and I have missed my sleep.' Mrs Essex had heard the wheels of a hansom, but she was already on the upper flight of stairs before the front door bell rang.

And this was the first Sunday evening on which Mark Gurdon did not stay to supper.

Chapter Twelve

A man feels his rejection either in proportion to his depth of feeling for the woman, or in proportion to his depth of feeling for himself; without severity it may be said, usually the latter.

With Mark it was strongly the latter, and a little of the former mixed in.

He had really admired Margaret very much; he was greatly puzzled to understand why she had not admired him. He couldn't suppose it was because he was poor that she would not marry him, and he equally could not suppose it was because she couldn't love him; he therefore declined upon the supposition that it was because he had not given her time enough to discover his good points. A girl – that is, a nice girl – is a very inexperienced creature, he told himself, and no doubt she had known so few men in her beautiful, carefully supervised life, that she was not able to see how superior he was to most other fellows from whom she might have expected proposals. He was a gentleman, and looked like one (a great advantage, this); he was poor, certainly, but he had a future; his manners and character – well, *he* didn't know anybody with better manners or character – this frankly and without any egotism, in fact, speaking as an outsider.

It is neither a man's nor a woman's fault that a proposal is usually such a fearful and ridiculous farrago. No woman with a sense of humour can listen to it without inward smiles – supposing that she is quite cool towards the man. If she is not quite cool towards him, she takes it in as well as the other woman who has no sense of humour. For falling in love blots out a sense of humour, of necessity, for the time being. Who looses his falcon to the flight, leaving his hood still on? Yet is the proposing man more closely hooded than the gay gosshawk.

Mark did remarkably well with his proposal, and made very fair use of his materials; it is not his fault that details of it sound silly: all real proposals sound rather silly, and no novelist in the world but can make up a much sweeter and more attractive one out of his own head.

He knew she was particular about some things, Mark said to her, when the moment came (he meant Leighton and his escapade by 'some things'). Well, he shouldn't like to brag about it, but – and then he made the well-known speech without which no proposal is really complete. He wore that air of humility and seriousness, combined with a rigid sense of right and wrong. He wouldn't like to call himself a *good* man; no man who sat beside Miss Essex could have the presumption to call himself *good*; but he would say that most men would call him a very decent specimen. He had 'lived 'to a certain extent (he was very careful to put in this ambiguous qualification, and tradition justified him; no man with any respect for himself ever leaves it out) – to a certain extent he had lived the life of an ordinary man of the world, but he had had his limitations, and there were lengths to which he had never gone. These were not things that she would understand, nor that he would like to speak of further, but, at any rate, he had lived a sort of life that enabled him to come into the presence of the woman he loved with his head up because he could show a clean record.

Margaret was, as I have insisted more than once, exceedingly inexperienced, and she was inclined to think this very fine; not knowing in the least what it meant, and further unaware that it formed part of the time-honoured shibboleth of proposal, she was decidedly impressed by it. And if anything could have won her to accept Gurdon, it would have been more of this high-minded and yet humble expatiation on his spotlessness.

Miss Essex looked prettier than ever, with her dark-grey, serious eyes holding two tears which never fell; and Gurdon was then moved to take her hand, very gently and respectfully. It was she who gave the pressure. 'Thank you – thank you so much,' she said, rather brokenly, 'for what you have said. I feel very much – I mean I am quite sure that – that – but, oh, please,

Mr Gurdon, don't think me odious, but I really never thought of you in that light, and I' – with a good deal more of the same.

Thus the moment of deepest emotion was reached over Gurdon's touching picture of the precise degree and shade of grey in which he had painted himself out of the devil's black paint-pot.

Margaret felt it to have been a pathetic and impressive moment in the interview, and in her own mind afterwards she called him 'poor fellow' once or twice: whether because he had not allowed himself a better time in this vicious old world, or because she could not hand him the reward of this praiseworthy self-denial, she never explained to herself, not having the analytical temperament.

As was natural, she saw less of Gurdon in the weeks that immediately followed, although it had been arranged that this was not to interfere with their 'friendship'. It was not likely to, as it in no way trenched upon that most mythical and shadowy of relations. Gurdon looked more serious, talked a little less at the club, and folded his lips ominously as he walked between the Colonial Office and his rooms. He turned in one night and heard part of a concert at St James's Hall, but came out because it seemed to him that he could not bear to hear a 'Polonaise' of Chopin's, which Margaret had played indifferently well, faultlessly given by 'some foreign fellow, with a beastly head of hair', as he mentally designated the eminent artist upon the platform. Coming out into Piccadilly, he ran against a man he knew slightly – that is, a man he had known slightly for a number of years. This individual, Lauriston by name, was a good-natured, weak-minded being, with a taste for what he called 'sport', and night clubs, and gardenias that reeked intoxicatingly of opoponax* as well as their own odious scent. Gurdon, being 'a serious-minded chap', had little in common with Lauriston as a rule, but he was just then at a loose end, and allowed himself to be hailed and his arm taken, and finally borne off in a fit of overdone chumminess to see something of which 'ten stone', 'six rounds', and 'a purse', formed descriptive elements. As a matter of fact, Gurdon would just as soon have sat at the National

Sporting Club, and clapped feebly, and listened to cheers, either raucous or affectedly treble, as he would have done anything else. In his own belief he was a badly cut-up man; but he hoped he was 'taking it as a man ought'; without going into this point, he was certainly taking it as a man often does. He sat in silence, with a half-smile of satire on his face, and watched Lauriston hang over the peacock-plush edge of the box, as he exchanged the time of day with fat gentlemen in exceedingly tight check suits and a tendency to a display of Parisian diamonds upon their ties.

It was late enough when Mark found himself passing along Piccadilly on his way to his rooms in Ryder Street. Already the impression of his unusual evening was passing out of his mind; in his younger days Mark had seen as much of that sort of evening as a steady fellow ever does, and he took it very calmly. Champagne in a big tumbler did not matter greatly to him. He was not unconsciously observant, as he had once told Margaret; the scenes of Piccadilly passed him by, or he shook them off casually, and entered, although unwillingly, upon his private gloom again.

Suddenly, when he had passed one woman, a shaft of recollection shot into his mind, and he looked round instinctively. The recollection was accompanied by some revulsion of feeling, but he turned with an impulse and raised his hat.

'Miss Lemuel?' he said. It was as much a protest as a question, and for once the face that met his had no smile.

'Well, I never!' she exclaimed in surprise; 'to think of its being you!'

'No,' he replied; 'to think of its being you! Why are you out alone like this? How are you in England? Where is your father?'

'Ah, well, that will be the whole story if I tell you all that, won't it?' She smiled now, but it was half-heartedly. 'We're in England because father has a job here. He came over to sit to Gilford for his "Death of Greek Art".'

'Well, but how are you out at this time of day? But perhaps I am not minding my own business as I ought?' his tone became reserved.

'Perhaps you aren't. I'm looking for father, if you want to know. Father has been drinking a good bit lately, and I'm not sure how he'll get through with this affair of Gilford's, unless I keep a pretty tight hold on him. The landlady fired us out of our lodgings today, and I got all packed and taken to a friend's – well, she's the charwoman who cleans Gilford's studio; and then father said he'd go and have a look round, and come back sharp for me when he'd settled something. I waited till about one o'clock, and then I knew something had happened, so I've been going round the dens.'*

She told all this very simply, and it was obviously only the inconvenience of her father's action, mixed with a fear that he would not be able to take up his 'job', that disturbed her. As they walked on together, Gurdon reflected quickly. Though he had met her half a dozen times in Paris only, and they had never talked much, he had an inexplicable liking for this girl. Used to roughing it she might be, but he could not allow her to walk alone down Piccadilly when he was there to prevent it. He looked down at her, on to the top of her shabby little hat, as it proved.

'Take my arm,' he said curtly. 'Your father was to look for rooms, you say? What if he has found none – where have you to go?'

'Nowhere,' was all her answer.

'Well, we must devise something. Is it not possible he may have returned to the charwoman's while you have been out looking for him?'

'Yes, he might have done.'

He could tell that she thought this very unlikely.

'Well, let us get into a cab and go there at once. Is not that the best thing to do?'

She admitted that it might be; and even though he could have put her into a cab and sent her off, he believed it his duty to see her safely even to that poor shelter. He hailed a cab, and they drove away together down to Kensington.

On the way, she plucked up her spirits, and told him many things that had happened in Paris since the winter when he had been there. At the end of May, Leighton had gone to Spain for the summer. When he returned, Arsénie had made other arrangements, since when Leighton had ceased to live at his studio, and had removed to a *hôtel meublé*.* He had become so extravagant that he had been obliged to have another man share his studio. His bill at the restaurant where he fed grew so large that he had had to move on to another. He had an arrangement at the artists' colourman's* to give him all his studio studies in return for material, and he had taken to working his *Académies** in oil colours instead of charcoal, painting in a tiger-skin and a drift of muslin afterwards, and calling tilem 'Après le Bain', 'Belle Baigneuse', and kindred titles.

All this chatter rippled pleasantly through Gurdon's mind, and, combining with the motion of a good cab, soothed him considerably. Cara Lemuel had a sharp and amusing tongue; often he was moved to a tired laugh at what she said; and when she took his hand and thanked him for being so good to her, it seemed only natural to put an arm round her thin shoulders with a comforting pressure. Altogether, he did not mind much how long this drive lasted.

But at length, in some of the narrow slummy byways near Queen's Gate, the cab drew up, they got out, and Cara undertook to find the door.

Gurdon stopped irresolutely for a second, then he told the man to wait, and followed her.

Chapter Thirteen

Old Lemuel had not come in. That was the first thing that struck Gurdon when he passed upstairs behind Cara. The key was below the mat just where she had placed it, the paraffin lamp was smelling as it had done ever since she turned it down hours before. They sat down opposite one another in the stuffy, evil-smelling little room.

'What can have happened to father? Oh, there must have been some accident!' Then she cried. She was that simple sort of creature that cried unrestrainedly and exuberantly when she was sorry, even as she laughed when she was glad. She dropped her face into her hands with a howl. Her short brown curls parted from the back of her neck, and fell forward in a thick shock at each side. The pointed girlish shoulders shook in a convulsive way. The backs of her narrow arms, pressed to her sides, had something young and pitiable about them; she was a horribly lonely, forsaken little thing. Gurdon made a quick step towards her, and patted her reassuringly on the back.

'Come, this won't do,' he said, with the exaggerated cheerfulness one uses to a child. 'What is the good of making up your mind that the very worst has happened? Depend upon it, your father is with a friend somewhere. There, that's right: be a woman.'

He might have kissed her, perhaps, but the thought of Margaret, whom some weeks ago he had dreamed of kissing, prevented him for the moment. Instead, he essayed more practical comfort. He found a spirit-lamp among her belongings, and with a little encouragement she produced some cheap red wine, which he heated and made her drink. She sat beside this meditatively for a little, then she raised her crying face, which had a prettiness about it in spite of tears and reddened eyelids.

This time, as he looked at her, no thought of Margaret occurred to him: his love for her had been compounded of idealised passion and fancy – they are very poor wear.

With her jacket off, and in some soft, limp sort of brown material, Cara looked pretty. Her dark skin, ripe colour, and easy eye had a single meaning. There are some women in the social state, as it is at present, fitted exclusively for 'the oldest of all professions for women'. They are to be met in all ranks of life. What sort of wives do they make? What sort of sweethearts? What sort of mothers? Whosoever selects them for a position of any permanency is mistaken. Women of abnormal sensuality, of incurable lightness, are private scourges. In a ballroom, for example, they will exercise every one of the arts and lures that have only one intention, then they will step into their carriages and sweep away with a final glitter in their lascivious eyes, and the poor creature in the street, whom they would not touch, is their victim.

The friends of women are not wise to declare that none are born scorpions.

That is the dark side of the picture. Of the light side and its effect, Gurdon is an example. Since his refusal by Margaret Essex, he had been fighting down a severe attack of passion; this night on which he came across Cara had sensually roused him. Under his cold, calm, measuring nature were buried smothered fires, on whose embers no wind of circumstance had yet blown strongly. His sensuality, as in other words he had told Margaret, had been slight; he made the mistake of imagining that he had resisted such temptations, whereas they had, in reality, never come his way, and he had never felt or seen them. He had carried what he called 'decency' to the chilliest business pitch, in a gentlemanly manner – that is, in the manner usual to a fastidious gentleman. The time came when, standing opposite Cara, he remembered only one thing; remembered with the greatest astonishment the means he had taken in the past to work himself up to the pitch of carrying through certain experiences with some air of relish. His training, his carefully nurtured ideas upon these subjects, had led him, even when alone, in his own mind and memory to banish the recollection of moments of almost wholly forced abandonment. He conceived a great horror of that old self of his; it passed over his mind as a wave: whether he had found anything better or not might be a question, he felt that his old feeling had been wrong. His brain worked with the spasmodic, whirring activity of the roulette wheel. The girl was in his arms without his having consciously taken her in them. Before passion quite swamped reason, he was questioning her hurriedly, in a voice whose very tones were quite new to him. The answers she made, which were an encouragement to passion, would have wounded love; but Gurdon was not in a condition to see distinctions, or to give feelings names. Things themselves are infinitely less confusing than the names they go by. One may recognise the thing itself, and one may even understand and feel familiar with it, but, over and above this, one must know its exact name. This difficulty is increased because things are not equally well named. The appositeness of all names to the objects and feelings they describe is nothing like so obvious as the appositeness of the title pig for the animal pig; for, as the old lady remarked, anybody could see for himself it was a pig.

The moment you leave the dry-land region of pigs and suchlike easy instances of careful and adequate nomenclature, you set forth upon a turgid sea of difficulties. It is the things that swim dimly below the surface of the thick water that are so hard to recognise and to name. Numberless people, be it said, sail out and never suspect the existence of these things; to them they are unthinkable. Others are conscious of them, but avoid the effort of clear comprehension and classification; to these they are unnameable. And a larger body of people than either of these, or indeed both these put together, are content to name them wrongly and confuse one hopelessly with another; to these they are undistinguishable. Such things as these, that fin slowly through the gloom of deep green waters, are chiefly feelings. There are among them passion, cruel and kind; desire, physical and spiritual, the same in form, but differing utterly in clearness of colouring: the one swimming on his belly in the mud, the other undulating through the bright weed, where the light of day shines down. If love, the flying fish, drop among them for a space, straightway he is confused to his own hurt until he swoop upward into the air again. The psychologist with his water-telescope is apt to be as wrong as anyone, and this has made many sensible and clever people decide that it is better to sit upon the shore beside the pig – who is so like a pig that you cannot mistake him; or, if you sail over the water, to keep your eyes lifted to the clouds of tradition, superstition, and legend. It will be a good day when one shall arise and tell us whether it is happier to live than to know, and at what level we should keep our dim, imperfect human eyes, as we pass about in the world that we think was made for us and that we have improved for ourselves. If Gurdon's case could have been put before Margaret Essex and Gallia Hamesthwaite – poor Gallia, away with her sick mother in Algiers, living a life of pulses and temperatures, and utterly divorced from her previous interests – how differently they would have seen it! Gallia, whose watchword used to be 'Truth' – Margaret, whose watchword was 'Goodness'. And if it could have been put before Gurdon himself, whose watchword was 'Decency', or before Leighton, whose was 'Life, and don't be ashamed of it'?

Gurdon's justification for his action lay in the fact that he had been won from his even, decent life when he fell in love with Margaret Essex. The hopes that had then risen in him had altered the aspect of his mind. His emotional territory had been changed in character by the volcanic upheavals during those weeks of close intercourse. He had sat in the little Hammersmith drawing-room and watched Margaret's fine flower-like hands moving over the yellow keyboard of the old sweet Broadwood, and his cold nature had warmed and warmed as he looked.

> Ah, the throats of thunder!
> Ah, the dulcet lips!
> Ah, the gracious tyrannies
> Of her finger-tips!*

Or he had seen her singing. Margaret singing was a picture for the gods. Then they had talked a long time about all sorts of abstract matters; and the conversation had been of that curious kind which love directs, of which love is ever the under-note. Then, when he went into town again and sat at dinner by himself at the club, or read in his own rooms afterwards, the mist of Margaret's influence still hung in the air around him. It was not that she gave him any token of love, or let drop one word on which he could build, but she was gracious, smiling, and her reception of him was kind, and she would play and sing when he asked her, liking apparently to give him pleasure; liking, at any rate, to make music for one who seemed to love it as any musical-souled being will.

If he had been a man of high moral tone (instead of being what he was, a man of 'decent' moral tone), he might have had a quarrel against her for destroying the placid fabric of his daily life, and then turning him off, to weave the fragments of it in what pattern he could, accommodating the red thread of passion, of which he was conscious for the first time.

He had come through all the experiences of the single man who, loving one woman, alters and rearranges his future to admit her share in it; he had tuned himself up to the new pitch of marriage; he had fostered, nurtured, been glad of the new feelings that had come to him, and which in that particular connection were creditable and decent, and then – he had been sent away; sent away single and unsatisfied, with havoc in his heart. But the feelings were still there. He was softened, warmed, plastic, and single. Whereupon the girl Lemuel crossed his path, and attracted his quickened sympathies. Here was where he might give himself rein and be no wise to blame: he assured himself on this point before he took her, for, as he said to himself, he was not a blackguard. He did not love her, although, oddly enough, he told himself that he did; he did not, for if he had, he would have hated the French artist of whom she naïvely told him; as it was, that was his permission. And not having a mind that traced its inspirations to their sources, Gurdon was unaware that Margaret Essex was a more or less direct cause of his protection of Cara.

Chapter Fourteen

It is difficult to understand why, as Gallia Hamesthwaite sat
beside her dead mother, in the big bedroom of the white hotel
upon the hillside, she should have thought of Dark Essex. At a
moment so lonely that it seemed to her an iron gateway had
closed across the avenue of life, and she should never go any
farther down that avenue, this man, with whom, after all, she
had never been closely intimate, who had certainly never been
kind to her, seemed nearer to her than any other human being.
If there were anyone in the world whose hand-clasp she would
have been passionately glad of, that person was Essex.

He had not been very often in her mind during the three
months' sojourn in Algiers; she had, during that time, thought
almost ceaselessly of her mother. Lady Hamesthwaite had not
benefited by the change; she had seemed wonderfully feeble,
with an unexplained, gentle, sweet-natured feebleness, which
grew only more evident day by day. In the mornings, Gallia had
walked beside her invalid chair; in the afternoons she had taken
her place in the comfortable European victoria which had been
sent over from France for their use. In between whiles she
seemed to have read aloud an infinitude of novels and books of
travel, looking up frequently to see if her mother's cheeks were
flushing with fever, or if she appeared ready for a little sleep.

At first Gallia had provided herself with books that interested
her more, and when the poor lady laid her head back on the
cushions and closed her eyelids, Gallia had been wont to dip
into these more congenial volumes. But after a time she could
not give them her attention, and she put them aside and sat
quietly in her place, letting her eyes wander to and fro between
her mother's face and the view from the window of the white
town down the hill.

When Lady Hamesthwaite's illness became more marked, when she had to send for her father, her thoughts and her daily life became confused: she lived in a dream. She could not have remembered, at the end of the day, whether some scene by her mother's bedside had happened in reality, or whether her brain had pictured it for her in a terrified foresight into what was coming upon them.

'And most of the time while she was well, I lived away from her, and thought it a great thing to follow out my own life and my own ideas. Why couldn't I have postponed that? I shall have such a long time for my own life and my own ideas, and I have had so short a time with mother! But I don't think I am ever going to care for the things I used to care for! Perhaps it is really right, after all, to sacrifice oneself to other people and live for them – but to me that has always seemed so immoral.'

Poor Gallia sighed away the wreckage of her creeds, and devoted herself, as whole-souledly as though she had never had any, to the duty and the privilege of nursing her mother, to whom she felt herself almost a stranger.

And Lady Hamesthwaite died because she had to; died in a fit of beautiful, painless unconsciousness, with her daughter and nurse beside her, her husband in England, and no goodbyes or last words of any kind. On the next day, when the funeral was to take place, Gallia spent the long hours of the morning in the darkened room beside the coffin; spent it with her thoughts. She was not crying – had not cried at all. Tears, at moments of emotion, seemed to be more remote even than laughter from Gallia's nature. The habit of her mind reasserted itself, and she stared before her, following through winding ways the ideas that arose like phantoms and fled in front of her.

'What happiness or pleasure have I ever had from mother?' she asked herself honestly. 'What has she meant in my life – sweet woman that she was? Almost nothing! I have hardly known her, really; there has been no communion between our minds, and none in our lives. Now she is dead, and – unless remorse for what was quite right and should not have been helped changes me – the loss is hers. How is my life any different? If I am still honest, if I do not start to build up in my mind the notion that mother was everything to me, and that now she is gone, all is gone – if I don't teach myself that pious lie, my life will be just the same. Can I have ever loved her at all? If I had ever loved her, I must have shown it in some fashion – and I don't remember that I ever did. It would be far more comfortable and far more respectable to give way to paroxysms of grief now, to fling myself about, to shriek to her sweet body lying here, and say, "Mother, I always loved you, and I am finding it out too late!"'

The girl paused; she had a sudden impulse to do this, she had a sudden wonder if perhaps this was, after all, what she meant. But Gallia had been too long accustomed to tell herself what she felt, having decided that after an interview with what it was reasonable for her to feel, and she lifted her sad look from the coffin and went on with her thoughts again.

'All the time mother loved me; Aunt Celia knew, and her letters might have told me, only, somehow, I knew it. Why is all the sweetness and passion and exquisiteness confined to the side of one party to the contract; why is it so certainly sweet to be a mother – apparently no matter of *what* sort of child – and why has the child on its side no instinctive sense of the exquisiteness of parentage?' She mused a long time upon this theme, and then another thought rose before her, and she followed it, as before, through the byways of her strange mind.

'The charm of motherhood must be innate: it has nothing to do with the child, or how it turns out, or what it proves to be. It is started once for all at the child's birth-time, and every woman has the sense of motherhood according to her emotional capacity. A mother has those feelings, which are more than mere love, because she has done something for the child, because she has borne it. She has performed a sort of self-sacrifice, which I have always thought the most subtle kind of selfishness in the world. Motherhood is selfish after all. So it comes in with my belief that the highest sort of selfishness is the only true and good religion – the only one that really makes for goodness. A woman gets a good deal out of motherhood; more than she does

out of marriage: motherhood is, on the whole, better suited to
her than marriage, I believe.'

She got off her chair and looked into the coffin, which was
filled with flowers, save where her mother's exquisite hands
were crossed on her breast, and where her face, immeasurably
more beautiful than it had been in life, with the colouring still
perfect in its transparent delicacy, looked up at her with shut
eyes.

'Were you very happy with father, I wonder? or did you really
love my coming more than all the rest?' she asked gently and
wistfully of the quiet face. 'I wish you could have told me before
you went which is best – love or motherhood? At this minute,
mother, you are the most beautiful woman in the world; your
spirit may be gone from your body, but it has left its loveliest
reflection on your face. If only you could have told me that one
woman's secret!'

It was characteristic of Gallia that, in spite of her amazing
belief regarding selfishness and its continuous practice as the
highest form of virtue, the questions she framed just then were
entirely abstract ones. She was not thinking of love for herself,
she was not remembering how she had said goodbye to it in that
upstairs room in Grosvenor Place. She was asking because she
would have liked to know. Perhaps she thought her mother's
spirit might have lent her some beam of the illumination it must
by that time have found in the place whither it was gone.

She was called away to receive her father, who had been
telegraphed for several days before, and, travelling with greatest
possible speed, had arrived too late.

He looked a very broken man indeed, as he advanced into the
sitting-room and met his daughter. One look at Gallia's face
told him his wife was dead, and he could for the moment only
take her two hands, and with his head turned away to hide his
grief, press them with the terrible shuddering pressure of a man
in the first throes of grief.

She took him silently to the room, and, closing the door, let
him find his way through the dim light to his wife's coffin.

In two hours he came out, but she did not see him; he had

gone to his own room, and was to be left undisturbed till the funeral started, so his man brought word.

So Gallia went back to be companion to the dead woman till the narrow door should be shut that was to close her from this world – and it was then that the yearning arose in her for the hand-clasp of someone she loved – and she thought of Dark Essex.

She had no grudge against him that he did not love her, and, on the whole, she had forgiven him the method in which he had explained this to her. It made no difference to her love for him, which was deep, had not grown from liking, and was unaffected by manifestations of dislike; which was also entirely without vanity or egotism, and had no support from his admiration or love of her; which was, therefore, if one may judge by its immunity from these earthly characteristics, the best kind of love there is.

If, by some impossible occurrence, he could be with her for five minutes! If, without speaking, she could have him clasp her hand firmly for one moment!

'I believe I should even be able to bear it if he were a little sorry for me. I wonder if it would touch him to hear that someone – anyone whom he knew – had lost her mother? I wonder if he would give the news one second's pity?'

She heard them in the adjoining room walking about, waiting for her to come out.

'Yes, I think he would be different now, and also – I *know* he wouldn't. Goodbye – for just now, mother: it has not all been for nothing. If you loved me all my life, some time, no doubt, we shall meet, and I will love you. I would have loved you if you had been my child, and perhaps, when I am a mother myself, my child may be like you, and I shall love it, and make the score even in that way.'

She took one of the white roses that lay near her mother's hands and kissed it, and began to put it inside her dress; then she stopped and looked at the slim bud again.

'Now, why do I do that?' she thought; 'it will die, and go brown, and all crumble, and I shall have it in a piece of paper somewhere, and forget where I've put it, and it will be forgotten, and get lost, or be dropped. No; one is not meant to remember – as we know by the sad case of all souvenirs. Mother, I'll give you back your rose. How much I remember you, I shall see in time,' – she smiled anxiously – 'but I will not give my humanity a chance to insult your memory.'

And these odd words were the last Gallia ever said to her mother.

Chapter Fifteen

Mrs Leighton was very sorry for her niece. 'It is the greatest possible misfortune for Gallia,' said the wise old lady. 'In time she would have come to know her mother, and, of course, to love her; and now – ah, it is a terrible misfortune.' For Mrs Leighton did not mistake for love the care and kindness Gallia had shown to her mother; she herself had a fairly clear perception of the bent of Gallia's mind, and so far she believed that the girl lived entirely within herself, and that she had no friends.

If it be not good for man to live alone, it is even worse for woman, the old lady believed. Gallia must now be three or four and twenty, and she had no one to love. For Lord Hamesthwaite, although a good and amiable and even a distinguished gentleman, was not the kind of man anybody would have made the mistake of loving. Besides, since his wife's death he had immersed himself more deeply still in politics. During the Easter recess he addressed meetings in the provinces, and worked even harder than while Parliament was sitting. Gallia lived with him in Grosvenor Place, but she was able to pursue an almost entirely separate existence in the big house, for there were no entertainments and few visitors during the first months of mourning. She had not returned immediately to England after the loss of her mother; she had spent two months very quietly in a small mountain town in the Alpes Maritimes. Here, accompanied only by her mother's maid, a conventional-minded French servant, who suffered untold tortures of *tristesse* and *ennui*,* she had lived and dreamed the days away; reading very little, and quite unconsciously hastening the departure of certain qualities of her youth and the charm that she had never recognised in herself and never used – unless dimly among her fellow-students at Oxford in the old days.

She liked to watch the mule traffic up the steep rocky path, she liked to look at the people pursuing their everyday avocations. She took no photographs, collected no flowers, made no sketches, put no impressions on paper. She merely walked and stood about, a curious smile of observance and silent kindliness upon her face. She made no charities, intruded in no kitchens, was known only by sight, and received none of the sentimental demonstrations of affection such as are histrionically proper to a situation of the kind.

Her maid, with thimble in pocket and scissors at her side, turned over sadly the four simple dresses that formed Gallia's entire wardrobe at this time. They were very strange dresses indeed. The dressmaker in Nice, a very important artiste, had had the fashioning of them, and never remembered having like restrictions imposed upon her. As they expressed in a measure Gallia's mind at this time, they have a certain interest. All were black, all were made in the same manner, absolutely plain in skirt, with bodice and band, high to the neck and long to the wrists, no fleck of white or flake of cambric anywhere at all. They tied at the throat with a black satin bow, and each was lined in the thickest satin of dove grey – though of this their wearer was possibly never aware: a dressmaker must have some excuse for the bill. In the cool mornings the maid laid out the cloth gown; on warm mornings the soft black linen. Also, according to the temperature of the evening, Gallia passed the last three hours of her day in velvet or in silk. She was far too clever a girl not to have taken great pains with her dress in her happier days, and she had a beautiful figure of the heaven-born kind; now, however, she watched with a sense of dreary amusement the careful routine of her bedroom so punctually performed.

'*Mademoiselle met?*'* occurred as regularly twice a day as though a galaxy of gowns was to be chosen from; and '*Celle de soie*',* Gallia would answer, or '*Celui en velours*',* as the case of robe or costume came up for decision.

It was in one of these same simple vestures that she made her appearance in her aunt's drawing-room, about a week after she came home. Mrs Leighton was herself in mourning, but it was a mourning most tastefully tempered to a garish world. She felt herself shudder when Gallia came in and sat among the pink and pale blue sofas, some of which were believed to have belonged to the very Louis* themselves. The old lady was seated in what she called her 'Salon Trianon',* and there was someone else in the room whom Gallia did not immediately observe; someone who wore the coolest of dresses of a June green shade, a muslin fichu, and a muslin hat with hop-wreaths on it; someone who sat near a green curtain, and was, that day, the very prettiest thing in Kensington.

'I think you know Margaret Essex?' said the hostess, as Gallia's severe folds settled themselves in the most frivolous of seats, and seemed to hold aloof from a carpet strewn with baskets tied with ribbons, from which pink roses poured luxuriantly.

The girls said something and shook hands. Each was interested in the other. Of course Margaret remarked that her brother knew Gallia well in Oxford.

'I think I feel a little alarmed about Miss Hamesthwaite's brain capacity in consequence of what he has said,' she added smilingly, and she felt even more alarmed at the look Gallia bent on her, although it was only a look of enquiry. But very soon Miss Essex went away, feeling certain that the aunt and niece had not met for some time, and guessing that Mrs Leighton must have much to hear from Gallia. Nothing surprised her more than Miss Hamesthwaite's simple request that she would come and see her in Grosvenor Place.

'I shall be so very pleased to,' Margaret had said cordially; and 'You will find that the very sweetest piece of china in London,' Mrs Leighton had remarked when the door closed on her pretty visitor.

'I thought it would be interesting to inspect a real girl,' Gallia said tranquilly; 'they are so very rare.'

And indeed a tropical butterfly couldn't have seemed a less familiar thing to her than did Margaret.

'And now, darling, tell me all about dearest Julia.'

Mrs Leighton had risen, and as she spoke she pressed her niece's firm shoulders tremulously, and sat down close to her and took her hand.

'Ah, my love, my love!' she sighed.

Gallia had known this interview was before her, and had been bracing herself for it for a long time. Only the knowledge that Aunt Celia had loved her mother, and particularly the knowledge that her mother had loved Aunt Celia, had enabled her to bear it as she did; but she marvelled at the awful sort of hardness in her voice and in her heart as she detailed the history of those weeks.

She thought afterwards that it was then that she had noticed the change in her that was afterwards so clearly marked; a change that altered her whole manner and character, no less than it altered her face and her dress. Mrs Leighton also noticed this change, and was more assured than ever of the misfortune Lady Hamesthwaite's death had been to the lonely girl. It was not that Gallia's face was older, but it had altered. Her idle, out-of-door mountain life had made her more beautifully healthy than usual, and her eye, instead of seeming clouded by the impossible problems she had a taste for considering, had the far outward look of a person who had thought through something, who had found foothold beyond. I think it was Herbert Spencer* who considered that a thinker should regard each solution reached, not as solid ground, but as a raft that would bear him for a time. Gallia, having swum strongly in fell currents, had climbed to a new raft.

An hour later, when most of the sorrowful particulars had been given, and silences were becoming frequent in the room, the butler made his appearance, and announced that Mr Gurdon was below, and had enquired if Mrs Leighton would receive him.

'Of course, dear, I have been seeing *nobody*,' said the old lady pathetically to her niece. 'Yes, Linton, say to Mr Gurdon that I shall be glad if he will wait a little in the library.'

'I am just going, Aunt Celia; I think I will say goodbye at once. You will come and see me soon, will you not?'

Noticing this leave-taking, Linton waited by the door to show out Miss Hamesthwaite; and thus it was that Gurdon, sufficiently familiar in the house to put aside some of the formalities, and standing therefore half in and half outside the library door, examining an amazing Moorish portière* that had been a present from Lady Hamesthwaite to her stepsister, saw a lady come downstairs of whose face and figure he caught just one astonishing glimpse. Gallia never noticed him at all – she was looking straight in front of her, and waiting while the butler looked for her carriage.

'What a magnificent girl!' said Gurdon to himself, as he followed a footman to the drawing-room.

Chapter Sixteeen

One side of Edwards Square is formed by the backs and belongings of houses fronting the Kensington High Street, the other two sides by very nice small houses looking into Edwards Square garden, the fourth side by a row of interesting buildings which were originally stables, and in some cases are so still, but of which many have been appropriated to other and more amusing purposes. They are buildings which differ fundamentally from the average of all London buildings in that they have a character; this character is of the most romantic and picturesque kind – it is to have no character. You look at them as you pass by – or at least you would look at them if you did pass by – and feel that anything might happen in them – that they might be anything; you know that Gaboriau* would have made thousands of francs out of any one of them; you wonder how they have escaped F. W. Robinson.* As a matter of strict fact, you never do pass by Edwards Square – nobody ever does. There is no reason to enter its quiet and very agreeable precincts unless you live there – unless your destination be your own front door, on one side of the Square or the other.

The few people, other than the residents, who have ever come there have done so because they have been lost, deservedly, in a vain attempt to find that non-existent thoroughfare between South Kensington and Kensington High Street. It was when once so lost that Gurdon came there. He entered the Square from the South Kensington side, and looked about him in his quick, clear-headed way. On the wide side of him stretched forward the row of quiet houses; on the other, in a horizontal direction, the row of buildings which were once stables. He worked upon the paving-stone with the ferule of his umbrella in a moment of thought. Then he turned upon his left, walked down past the buildings, stopped for a moment to copy the address on a notice-board above one of them, turned back upon his tracks, and was in the High Street in two minutes.

The building that bore that notice of 'To let' lay about the middle of the row. It had a coach-house door painted green; a harness-room door in the same colour, and above this second door a window, which had obviously replaced the flap-door to a hayloft. There was also a good skylight, which showed signs of having been improved. In a word, a stable made into a studio.

On an evening when the blackened trees and shrubs were heartening up in a pale green manner inside the garden railings; when sparrows were chirping in the trees in a way to suggest only the sharpening of dozens of slate-pencils, combined with the hearthstoning of dozens of steps, there mixed with these indications of a metropolitan spring evening, the cricket-note of a guitar, that seemed to be played in a purposely subdued manner by a very skilful hand. In chorus with the guitar, two siskins* in a cage beside the coach-house door woke up and began in an irresponsible way a sort of tune to which they were unaccustomed. Whether the guitar, or a shaft of late sunlight that invaded the cage, had aroused them, one could not know; but soon the guitar ceased, the door opened, and a girl came out and reached up for the cage, and bore the siskins, in a futile flutter, to the room within.

Inside, the harness-room wore the air of a hall or anteroom, and a curtain crossed the approach to the coach-house or studio, which was a long, narrow apartment, matchboarded and painted green, and could not have made a single brougham feel more at home than the young woman and the tea-kettle and the sofa looked.

The wooden platform on castors, which had supported a model in a chair many times, was covered with a mattress and some rugs and cushions, and made an odd sort of lounge, which travelled slightly when one sank upon it.

Hereon the girl flung herself, and picked up the guitar angrily, like a person who, although tired of its companionship, had nothing else to talk with.

The guitar spoke, in response to her sweeps and clutches upon its strings, and her ill-trained but effective little voice scraped out the phrases of a gipsy song. In between the verses, which were innumerable, the guitar stormed, sobbed, or twittered, as demanded by its wilful friend, with a sympathy which, though mechanical, seemed spontaneous and personal to itself.

Cara Lemuel's playing was as unlike that of the myriad young women who play the guitar 'a little' as any playing could well be. Her mother had been a Spanish gipsy before she became a model, and long before the days of which she had any memory, the girl had carried the shabbiest of tambourines among the café tables in shabby parts of Seville.

The two siskins, now hung on a nail upon the inside of the big coach-house door (which was no longer made to open) shrugged their wings as they listened, and put away their bills safely for the night amid a plumage of which at this evening hour they made the very most. Tiring at last of her playing, the guitar was laid aside, and Cara slept as easily and simply as she had often slept before on the sofas of other studios in Paris. When Gurdon came in some hours later, she was just awaking, and her awaking was as easy and smiling as her sleep. Irritation marks the waking of most western-bred beings; smiles dawned slowly upon the features of the southern Cara.

'Don't move, little woman, you look so pretty,' Gurdon said, as he threw his bag into a corner. 'I've come for a couple of hours only, and have to dress and be at the other end of London by half past eleven. Any coffee?'

She pointed lazily to a covered pot upon the stove, and he found himself a cup upon a shelf and sat down beside her. She did not talk much, but she smiled a great deal, and was caressing in a very attractive manner, and her black-brown hair, which was of a locky character, heavy, full of form, and making effective masses no matter how arranged, fell against his cheek as she kissed him, and had a spicy scent about it which was delicious and a little intoxicating.

'I have a new song for you,' she said; 'at least I have

remembered it bit by bit, and I expect my mother used to sing it. What a pity you don't know Spanish!'

'You shall teach me Spanish. I learn languages pretty easily, and it will be a good thing for me to know a little Spanish.' Gurdon's mind, characteristically, saw the proposition at once in the light of its possible advantage to himself.

'Well, now, I'll tell you. This is the song of a gipsy girl who loves a man not of her own people, and she is saying all the time, in each verse, how he is so white and so fair and that sort of thing, and the chorus always is – oh, how would it be in English? It won't sound a bit the same, but she always sings –

> So in the chestnut avenue,
>   All the day I wander, wander;
> This side of the hill path
>   The brown chestnuts grow;
> And white magnolia blossoms shine
>   In the dark gardens down below.

Oh, I've made a rhyme, haven't I? Well, now, I'll sing it to you. First, it's about the lover, all very quiet like this.'

She bent over the guitar and picked a mournful prelude from the strings; then her voice, dramatic in spite of, or perhaps because of, its want of training, rose in the recitative of the verse part. Gurdon listened; he was passionately fond of music, or rather of singing, and he looked as much as he listened. Cara's small curved brown fingers, thin and taper, with the articulations appearing whitish through the skin, skipped nimble above the strings, and she bent lower over the neck of the instrument, her hair falling in free locks from her head; but for the chorus head and hair were jerked backwards, the guitar was clutched passionately against her body, and the sadness of the weird gipsy plaint rang out in a very agony of descriptive music.

'Sing that bit that begins "*Yo soy la castaña marrón*" again,' cried Gurdon; 'that's the bit I like!'

'Ah, that's "I, the brown chestnut",' Cara said, smiling with immense fascination in his face. Then she shot from her low seat and stood a dozen feet away, in the attitude so peculiar to

Spanish women, the shoulders and head thrown far back, one foot advanced, her guitar seeming to strain upon the troubadour ribbon that passed round her right shoulder. Thus she sang the chorus with a stormy melancholy; at the end, sweeping the guitar behind her back, where her left hand held it head downwards, she stepped the opening movements of one of those Spanish dances, so haughty, so restrained, so solemn, that they seem to double the burning of the fire beneath.

She was below the medium height, but with the national port of head and shoulders, she seemed a queen in stature, and the effect was electric when a few swift paces brought her with a laugh to Gurdon's feet. Neither of these two loved the other, but passion was a religion with the half-Spanish creature, and religion will soon become a habit. To toy dramatically and convincingly with the simulacra of strong feeling is just as successful, is perhaps more successful, a means of arousing passion in another, and Gurdon found an unnatural *abandon* made easy to him by the wiles and magic of the girl's walk, or song, or strange dance. He took the guitar from her neck, and caught her in his arms and feasted upon her face.

Chapter Seventeen

The friendship which grew up between Margaret Essex and Gallia was wholly of Miss Hamesthwaite's making; from the first and to the last she frightened the picturesque Margaret considerably. Margaret would have confessed to an interest in her conversation, would have admitted volubly a deep admiration of her manner, mind, and appearance, but would have been conscious all the time of the courage of a tortoise-shell guinea-pig when she found herself in her friend's society. The turn in the Park which they were now taking, Margaret having lunched – timidly and *tête-à-tête* – in Grosvenor Place, was entirely Gallia's idea, and had been undertaken with the excuse of seeing Miss Essex on her homeward way; but the unlooked-for apparition of Gertrude Janion was an accident, and the sort of accident that Margaret deplored.

As the three walked along together, they presented the oddest contrast: Gallia, in the middle, was as severe as black of the plainest cut could make her; Margaret, on her left, was draped rather than clothed in Madonna blue, softened with lace the colour of old stucco, and wore a hat with wide black eaves arching over her palely brilliant hair, the whole deftly combined to create the air of inevitability that a really becoming gown will ever present.

Beside these two Miss Janion felt happy that she knew how to dress, and was at that moment, as at every moment of her public appearance, dressed to perfection. To be fashionably clad is given to many women, and often a perfectly original personality is concealed by clothes which are original only within the strictest limits; it is unusual to issue from the hands of Félix or of Worth* in a garment which, besides taking rank as their latest and most wonderful creation, has also the added merit of describing exactly its wearer's mental plane. The Janion girl was in herself exactly what her clothes looked; as it happened, neither Worth nor Félix had the credit of her, though she would have disgraced neither. It was her proud boast that she dressed on £250 a year, 'for everything, my dear girl,' and she could certainly, as regards 'smartness', have cut out women with three times that sum at disposal.

She was a small, very neatly built person; nothing was exaggerated about her figure. Nature had been friendly towards her, and even seemed to know her aspirations from the beginning, and to sympathise with them; had dowered her with a waist that needed wonderfully little compression, and bore that little remarkably well; had given her a beautifully modelled throat, bust, and arms: the throat and arms she left alone and was glad of; the bust she enhanced artificially, in obedience to the prevailing notion that a young woman shall not await nature's own development.

With regard to features, she had nothing to complain of; she was not really pretty, and so the effect of prettiness which she never failed to make was all the more meritorious. The acute angle of her jaw, which made her face, broad at the brows, come off to a very sprightly point, was much in her favour; so were her eyebrows, which had a double curve in that the sharp, closely feathered ends of them turned upwards again. Certainly her eyebrows were most piquant. As to complexion, she would tell you frankly that she had always found the 'Norwich man' best of anyone; you could rely on his things, and they were not so madly expensive as some of the other people's.

'He doesn't sell that Sauce Béchamel sort of stuff for evening wear, and then swear that it's not a paint, only a "cream", as most of the other people do,' she would exclaim, in her very high, shrill little voice.

Perfect frankness about these various aids to beauty was Miss Janion's line.

To Gallia, such a woman was what the discovery of the ass-like horse of the Central Asian plains was to Przevalsky:* she listened eagerly, greedily, with her face all lighted up, to the stream of chatter about laces and people and powder, and silk-covered hair-pins, and the last book, and Mrs Tree's* dresses in the last play, and the new system of paying a yearly sum to a milliner and taking your hats on hire by the week or fortnight, and other kindred topics, very brilliantly touched on. Margaret, her grey eyes shining, her face beneath the delicate, sunbeamy colour which was its most usual surface, listened in horror, wondering vaguely what on earth Miss Hamesthwaite would think, and if she would take Gertrude to be a type of all her companions.

So engrossed were the three, that in the crowd they missed seeing two well-known faces; a rare thing for the Janion girl, who had the fashionable trick to a nicety, of seeing and not seeing everybody at her own expedient whim.

'Hullo! A queer team for a troika!' exclaimed Lauriston, who had just joined Gurdon and Dark Essex, when his eyeglass focused the backs of the three girls.

Gurdon was on horseback (he rode every day while he was in London, because all the men who succeeded in climbing into big places in the Services rode every day while they were in London, and were in the habit of saying they could never have lived without it). He looked round quickly.

'Your sister, Essex, and I believe –'

'Miss Hamesthwaite in the middle,' said Lauriston glibly, 'and the Janionette on the off. Think I'll catch up with them and hear how they are getting on. I've often wanted to know Miss Hamesthwaite, and the little girl will introduce me.'

'Should we all move down?' Gurdon inquired tentatively.

'I shall reserve the pleasure for another occasion,' Essex said, with his stone smile.

Gurdon had by this time thought that more suitable surroundings might be found for his introduction to Lord Hamesthwaite's daughter; so Lauriston strolled off alone, and, having become exceedingly short-sighted, owing to his lifelong habit of insisting that he was so, failed to discover the trio, and brought up ignominiously beside a very brilliantly-painted and high-hung barouche, the occupant of which would have been (so she always declared) a marchioness in actual fact, if divorce were on a sensible basis in this foolish old country.

'Your sister is a great friend of Miss Hamesthwaite's?' Gurdon said, looking down very keenly upon, as it happened, the dazzling disc of Essex's silk hat.

'They meet pretty frequently, I believe; but I fail to apprehend why either of them should take up Miss Janion.'

'I have met Miss Janion, I fancy, at a ball,'

'A subscription ball.'

'I believe it was.'

'It certainly would be.'

'Is a subscription ball to be made a cause of reproach in your exclusive mind?' Mark asked lightly.

'Far from it. I have, all unknown to her, a deep and lasting admiration for Miss Janion. She is the most unaffected woman I know, save one. She is incurably vulgar, she is shrewd enough to know it, and yet I have never found her making the least attempt to disguise it. She doesn't pose. My sister does pose a very little, and it comes near to spoiling her. She thinks she cares for art, but that will pass off quite satisfactorily when she marries.'

'You are against a woman having an interest, then?'

'My dear Gurdon, I don't believe I have even got an opinion about women. A quiet man doesn't need to have, nowadays. Women have taken men's opinions of them for granted, and there is nothing they seem to quote with more freedom. But I know,' he yawned, quite genuinely, 'I'm on the safe side. I'm "against" nothing. If I were, it might be against a woman having more than two interests – herself and the man she marries.'

'And her children?'

'You will not prevent a woman having an interest in her children, if she has been woman enough to have had an interest in herself and her husband. And as far as my observation goes, the posing woman will care for her children too. She can't afford not to. Maternity is a strong pose with your platform woman. She has to be regarded as a "thorough wife and mother", it fills the cheap seats so. Yes, women have a lot of courage. But I don't believe the woman breathes, who, if she didn't care for her children, would have the courage to say so. Which brings us back to Miss Janion, who never poses.'

'If my memory of Miss Janion is correct, she wore a very low dress at the ball; I remember this because she asked me if I thought it too low, and I was a good deal embarrassed.'

Essex laughed; just a couple of bars of deep, rich-noted laughter, then he drooped his head, leaned upon the railings, and went on making a little mound of sand, and burying a small tuft of grass with his foot.

'But, as I was going to say, she is nothing like so attractive a woman as your sister.'

Essex raised his eyes with a serious expresssion in them. It was as though he had half expected Gurdon to discuss his sister in the same tone they had used concerning Miss Janion, but Gurdon had no such idea, and Essex, reassured, spoke in the way and with the conviction he always showed when he mentioned his sister.

'She is the only type of woman left us, capable of attracting in the romantic way,' he said thoughtfully. 'This sort of subject comes easy to me just now, because, as I think I told you before we left the club, my publishers recommend the expansion of that monograph of mine into a book, and I've been working upon it for the past two months at a quiet little place I've found in Surrey. In *The Comparison of Emotion in the Human and other Animals*,* most of the arguments against Darwin are drawn from an unprejudiced consideration of the emotional capacity in women. I have decided to recognise three kinds of attraction, although I might reasonably decide against this division into three. Intellectual attraction – very common nowadays, and responsible for at least half the marriages in middle-class society, where marriage still remains and will remain a matter of attraction. Physical attraction – accountable for all the other marriages in the world (not counting those of position, interest, and so on, which don't concern me, as they are marriages of no attraction) – accountable for all the others, Gurdon, except a small number still founded on romantic attraction. My sister

Margaret is a type of the sort of woman who makes that last form of marriage possible. To be romantically attractive, a woman has got to be innately good (I am using such words in the old-fashioned sense, you understand) and innately beautiful; but beyond this, as we have hounded the old timidity and simplicity and insipidity and such other idities from our doors, she must be semi-talented and semi-independent. There is a rage for talent and independence nowadays; a girl can't have the commonest sort of success, poor thing, unless, forsooth, she does something independent!'

'I agree with every word you say of your sister.'

'It's a pity she happens to be my sister, for the sake of argument, but I refer to her merely because she is a picture, an etching of the type – a silver-point.'*

'She is indeed; but I was going to say that I think her clever. Her music, her painting, are ever and ever so far above the amateur average, you must admit?'

'Oh, I do; but so is every other girl's, you know.'

'Well, I don't know. Miss Janion now, I'm sure, if she plays, it's in just the usual way.'

'Doesn't play a note, doesn't paint a stroke. You don't appreciate Gertrude. Her talent is to be better dressed than any one else, and she always is, in my judgment.'

'I am becoming anxious to know more of this shining example of the modern girl.'

'Then you had better hasten forward, and if they haven't had enough of it, you'll meet them coming up. I'm going to the Natural History Museum to talk to an old friend who has written to me. Will you dine with me tomorrow? A note in the morning will do. I'm only in town till Saturday.'

'Devonshire again?'

'No, Surrey. An inn three hundred years old; everything three hundred years old except the cat and the bitter ale.'

'Well, I envy you.' Mark gathered up his reins.

'You don't now, but if you were seedy, you would yearn for a week in my village.'

Chapter Eighteen

'Oh dear, I believe I want my tea!' exclaimed Miss Janion, with the same manner, and certainly in the same key, that a green paroquet would have made a similar remark. The three oddly assorted companions had chosen three isolated chairs, which had the merit of being somewhat private, and yet commanding a fair view of the drive. 'There's nothing I look forward to with the same yearning anticipation as tea. I begin about three o'clock; I tell myself how delicious tea is going to be; at four, I console myself by thinking that I can ring for it a little early, and that will be a quarter to five. I don't think there is anything that excites me more than the thought of tea; and how beastly it always is when it comes!'

'And men think we get so much out of it!' Gallia said drily, having greatly appreciated Miss Janion's extravagant little speech.

'It's men who, by chaffing women about tea-drinking, have got up the idea of tea being such a godsend. There's a conspiracy among men to make women stick to tea and think they like it. Hear men sighing, "Ah, I wish I dare", when they steadily refuse it day after day. Catch them taking any!'

'I'm always trying new teas, and new ways of making tea,' put in Margaret. 'I think I sometimes enjoy it when it's very weak and has a great deal of cream and sugar in it.'

'Depend upon it, you only think so,' laughed Gallia.

'It's a woman's bitterest disappointment – tea and men,' Gertrude wound up sagely.

'I'm not a bit disappointed in men – on the whole,' Margaret declared.

'Nor am I,' from Gallia; 'I think men are quite good enough.'

'Good? You don't mean to say you think men good?'

'I don't think I mean that sort of good,' with a smile to Gertrude. 'But they are good-looking enough, and strong enough, and healthy enough. They compare favourably with women in these respects.'

Margaret had her eye fastened on Gallia's face.

'One has two views of men, I think: one of men in relation to the world – the world of war and letters and statesmanship and trade, and so on – and one has to admire them there; the other, of men in relation to oneself, and there it seems to me most important that they should be well-grown and healthy and sound – in wind, limb, and temper.' She ended up with a little laugh. Margaret was conscious of not understanding her, but Gertrude, being a person of absolutely no insight, replied glibly –

'I like men to be amusing and jolly, and of course as good-looking as possible. I don't think I mind much if they are what Miss Hamesthwaite calls sound.'

'But you would if you were going to marry them.'

'I don't know. But, any way, one can't marry them all.'

'But there are other women –'

'They've got to look out for themselves. And now that so many have taken up nursing, it can't be quite the slavery it used to be to have an invalid husband.' Miss Janion was quite unaware of being on the wrong track. 'I do think life – I mean domestic life – is beautifully easy now; one needn't do a thing oneself, one can get someone in! At home we are always getting people in. Papa has his masseur every day; mamma has her nursemaid – I mean maid-nurse; Alfred has his electric shock person and galvaniser* – he can't raise a slipper before eleven, when this person comes, and afterwards he's awfully larky until it wears off. Ella Lane, who lives next door, shares my hair man, who comes in. We get in the butler; we get in a woman – I think she's a lady – to do the flowers for parties. One needn't really have any trouble nowadays, or do anything; one can always get someone in.'

'It's the tendency today. In the next century we shall have

organised things more perfectly, and shall be able to get even more people in, in other capacities.'

'Well, hasn't there been a fuss lately about getting all the cooking in?' asked Margaret. 'I'm sure a central depôt for that would be a great blessing.'

'It would indeed. We may live to see that, but we shan't live to see the real advance; which will be the getting in of fathers and mothers, or rather husbands and wives to be fathers and mothers.'

Gertrude shrieked; Margaret was silent and startled.

'I was speaking quite seriously; and if you think, you will see that such a scheme would be eminently rational. The outcome of the present health movement must lead that way. People will see the folly of curing all sorts of ailments that should not have been created, and then they will start at the right end, they will make better people. How can we wonder that only one person in ten is handsome and well made, when you reflect that they were most likely haps of hazards, that they were unintended, the offspring of people quite unfitted to have children at all? There are people fitted, for instance, to be mothers, which every woman isn't; there are women fitted to bring up children, who may not be mothers. Think of this: a man may love a woman and marry her; they may be devoted to each other, and long for a child to bring up and to love; but the woman may be too delicate to run the risk. What are they to do? What would be the reasonable thing to do? Sacrifice the poor woman for the sake of a weakly baby ? No, of course not, but get in a mother!'

A moment's silence fell upon the three. Their brains were a little burdened, and no wonder, by this astounding piece of social reform.

'But why not adopt a child?' ventured Margaret at length.

'But it wouldn't belong to either of them, and they couldn't tell in what odious surroundings it had been born. Surely much more reasonable to get in a mother?'

A light dawned upon Miss Janion, and she began, 'But this strange woman –'

'She wouldn't be a strange woman; she would be a splendid,

beautiful, healthy, accredited woman, and probably physically very attractive. The man's sentiment, if he had any, would be greatly in her favour; men have wonderfully little sentiment, as their whole way of life shows, in a matter of that kind. He would have been able to indulge his very highest feeling in the choice of his wife. It would make enormously in favour of morality.'

'Do you think it would?' said Margaret.

'Surely; by making in favour of health, by making in favour of justice, by lifting a burden from the shoulders of the weak and placing it on the shoulders of the strong.'

'And the – the poor journeyman mother – would she like giving up her child?' the gentle Margaret asked again.

'It wouldn't be her child only, it would be his child, by agreement –'

'Now, I wonder, if one was married, whether one would *like* another woman supplying the baby element in the family?'

'If one were not strong enough to supply it oneself, Miss Janion, surely? And don't you see that if this plan were adopted, there would be far fewer delicate men and women in the world? The plan would be worked from both sides equally, and the strong, finely-bred children growing up happily, well distributed over the homes of the country, instead of there being eight in one and none in another, as is the case just now, these children would have a much better chance. People are not above 'getting in' a wet-nurse nowadays, and in the most casual fashion; it seems to me this is only a step farther.'

Again a silence – on Margaret's part a sunset-coloured silence; on Gertrude's a silence pointed by twitching lips and eyebrows; on Gallia's, the silence of a shrewd and hopeful saint.

'It sounds like treating the world as a sort of farm, and men and women merely as animals,' said Margaret, with some distress.

'Precisely my idea,' said Miss Hamesthwaite calmly. 'At present half the world is not as well treated as the best class of animals, and there isn't a political economist living who wouldn't say that if the increase of the lower classes could be taken out of their own hands and supervised on scientific lines, crime as well as a number of diseases would be stamped out. If it could only be done – if it could only be done!' Gallia's clear, earnest face, with the thin, dark line deep between her eyebrows, looked straight in front of her, and that was how Gurdon saw her, and again thought her magnificent, as he rode by, about thirty paces away.

'And what would you do with people like that in your world?' said Miss Janion, pointing to the brilliant barouche which was turning opposite them in order to take its beautiful occupant to the corner in time to see the Duchess.

'Who is it?' enquired Gallia innocently.

Miss Janion informed her with some ceremony. 'I really know her well by sight,' she added, 'because we both get our hair at the same shop – there is really no one like Hugo for hair-pin fringes.'

'I have no quarrel with her,' Gallia replied, with a certain bitter quiet.

'Vile creature!' sputtered the Janion girl.

Gallia looked shocked, and rose from her seat.

'I hope you don't mean that,' she said; 'you have the greatest possible reason to be grateful to her whole class and to pity them. I must go home now, I think.' She had looked at the sky and the trees' shadows, and then compared their time with her small black-enamelled watch.

'You should write about your ideas,' said Margaret, smiling up at her from under the black-eaved hat.

Gallia shook her head briskly.

'One would only be grouped with all the other women who are said to be leading the "Sexual Revolt",* and that would do the ideas harm, for no one would take them seriously.'

'But so much attention is paid to what women write now.'

Gallia smiled drily, and swept her eyes over the Park before bringing them to Margaret's face; then, taking her hand at the same moment she said –

'That's just it! What they say makes so much noise that nobody hears properly what it is. A woman who really feels these things shouldn't write about them now, until what they call the boom of women is over.'

'But couldn't she write under a man's name?'

'Men don't think these things, you see.'

'No men?'

'I don't think any man.'

'But how is that?'

'Because' – Gallia smiled a little, and then her face grew wistful as she returned her answer, unspoken, to her own mind. 'Goodbye, Margaret. Don't dislike me on account of this crusade against the copy-book. Goodbye, Miss Janion.'

'It's been an awfully jolly afternoon,' remarked that sprightly young woman, as she and Margaret stood to watch the quiet figure in black go up the path. 'She *is* amusing,' she added heartily.

'She doesn't mean to be.'

'People so seldom mean to be, and so often are.'

'But she's perfectly serious in all she says and even more serious in the things she thinks and doesn't say.'

'Really, now? Do you think she can have been jilted or had a disappointment? It sounds like it, doesn't it?'

Chapter Nineteen

Gallia's life at this time was a very lonely one, and that, she would say to anyone who commiserated her, was its very best feature. She liked to be alone, at least she thought, like many other young people of her temper, that she liked it; but she was happier and better in every way when she was not alone, and her father, a man of small insight in domestic matters, but occasionally right in his judgments for all that, decided that she should not moon about the country home in Surrey for six weeks all by herself, but should persuade 'one of her young friends' (Lord Hamesthwaite was perfectly unaware that she had none – he believed that every girl had a number of young friends) to go down and spend the time with her.

'Very well,' Gallia had said, and she determined to see if Mrs Essex and Margaret would come.

'Quietly, of course,' Lord Hamesthwaite had added, with a sigh. 'No party. Quite quietly. And I have asked Shillinglee and Oswald – I think you have met Oswald? We are going to have a week's work upon the Bill. Later on Denyer will join me.'

'Has Mr Denyer left Africa, then?'

'My dear child, you surely remember the whole business of Denyer's leaving the Cape not six weeks ago? He is in the Auvergne at present for his health, but by the end of July he will be in England.'

Gallia nodded; she took no interest in the South African business and Mr Denyer, but it was impossible to take up a paper without coming upon a mention of her father's name and the name of Denyer in connection with the great question.

These few words were spoken at the beginning of the hot fortnight in June. There always is a hot fortnight every June in

London, and it was just beginning about the time that Lord
Hamesthwaite made known his summer plans to his daughter.

What a quiet summer it was going to be! how different from
the summers Gallia had always run away from in her mother's
lifetime, when a large political party was gathered in the
breakfast-rooms every morning, and important talks – talks
which were going to colour the Parliamentary business of the
day – went forward among the old-fashioned flower-beds; then
the quiet that fell when a midday train had borne all the political
tools and implements to the big London workshops. On
Wednesday nights, the immense dinner-parties at which Gallia
had sometimes been present; parties at which unexpected political constellations scintillated, and the working-man member sat
down with the nursing peer, and a satirical writer, some Tory
leopard, lay down with the Radical kid.*

It all seemed very far away now, and now that it seemed so
far away, Gallia wondered if she would not have done better to
be in the midst of it. She could be brilliant in society if the mood
was upon her; but in those days she had been so serious, because
so young, that the men who held the country's destiny in their
hand had appeared too frivolous for her.

'They never seemed to be interested in real things,' Gallia
explained to her aunt when she dropped in upon her to detail
her father's plans, and they got talking about past times
together. 'All they said and all they thought seemed so far away
from real things as they really are. It seems to me, that if you
live the perfectly engineered life of public men – put down by a
brougham in time to be picked up by a Pullman,* turned out of a
Pullman into a waggonette or a dog-cart; just time to dress for
dinner; just time to sleep before being called and dressed and
breakfasted; just time for a few words, quite lightly and unser-
iously spoken, and usually taking the form of a chaffing comment upon an opponent, or a good story of a mistake in one of
the Offices, or an amusing misunderstanding at one of the
Embassies; then the waggonette and Pullman and brougham
again, and the House for a few hours – what leisure have they
to look at real things as they really are? In the train men look at

the afternoon papers – or they read one of a mass of pamphlets from inside an elastic band. I don't see – unless they remember things they saw when they were boys and loitered about and birds-nested – I don't see how they are to know about any of the things that really are.'

'To hear these wild sentiments from your father's daughter!' cried the vivacious old lady in reply. 'Why, child, there is no particular occasion to know about things as they really are. Men in your father's position have no time for that, and it wouldn't advantage them the least bit if they had. They know most accurately, I am sure, about things as they are reported to be. They read and get up reports; and when you would have them looking out of railway carriage windows across flying fields –'

'Well, they might see something.'

'What in the world could they see? A few labourers going home, perhaps.'

'Or a few wood-pigeons,' interjected Gallia softly. Then, 'But surely laws are made to make things better than they are,' she went on, 'and if they don't ever –'

'My dear child, you are really too old to talk like that – in your position too!'

'Dear Aunt Celia, you must forgive me. You know I am very, very backward in all such things, having never paid them the least attention; but I think I am going to be more interested in papa's work now.'

'I hope you will sympathise with it, dear,' said Mrs Leighton gravely. 'It might be as well not to go so far as to be interested in it – that is a term that seems to represent so unpleasant an attitude nowadays – but to sympathise with it would be very graceful, dear, very graceful indeed, and very gratifying to your father, I am sure.'

Gallia smiled in her wistful manner, and passed to another subject.

'When will you come down to the Hall, Aunt Celia?'

'You really want to have me, dear? So good of you both! Well, I shall be a month at Aix, and – shall we say the early part of August?'

'Any time that suits you will do perfectly, of course. Papa mentioned this morning that Lord Shillinglee was coming down for a week – perhaps Mr Oswald too, on political business.'

'Have you ever thought, my dear Gallia, of marrying Lord Shillinglee?'

'Certainly I have not.'

'Ah! because in some ways it might suit very well.'

Gallia laughed. 'I don't know whom it would suit in any way,' she said; and added quickly, in order to change the subject, for on marriage Aunt Celia was dangerous, 'And Mr Denyer is expected.'

'At the Hall? You don't say so? It is always so difficult to get any information about public business. I never think of asking your father, unless I am prepared to pretend that I know already; and Mr Gurdon persists in saying that he knows no more than the pigeons in the courtyard. But Denyer has certainly played a great part recently, and I want very much to see the man himself.'

Mrs Leighton was referring to what was at that time 'the South African question'; it does not in the least matter which South African question. The Government had, as usual, quite scandalised one-half of the public either by its action or its inaction in the matter. Lord Hamesthwaite had been severely criticised, publicly and privately; then something had been taken back and something else explained away, and a great deal more ignored, and the whole matter was forgotten save by the people who were leisurely engaged in compiling a Blue Book* to be published in a few years' time; a Blue Book which might be used in Board Schools* as a model of the complete letter-writer.

'But I often feel,' went on Mrs Leighton, 'that Mark Gurdon – who has been in Africa and has his eyes so wide open – could tell me a great deal, but he will only dilate upon the "Karroo".' The door opened at this moment, and Gurdon himself almost anticipated the announcement of his name.

'So magnetically sympathetic of you to come in just now! Your name was upon my lips,' said Mrs Leighton, as they shook hands. 'Let me present you to my niece, Miss Hamesthwaite.

Dear Gallia, Mr Mark Gurdon, to whom I have become quite attached!' This was made very playful and complimentary, and something in the old lady's manner put Mark at his very best. The old lady's easy and genial artificiality acted like a sun upon persons who possessed the social art; they behaved delightfully in her rooms, and went away happy because successful. As for herself, it was her habit to remark that she was entirely satisfied with the manners of the present day, about which she heard so much complaint. There was all the courtesy that one could wish, if one merely gave it an opportunity to come out.

Gallia watched Mark carefully as he spoke to her aunt. She seemed to have heard of him often, considering that he was an unimportant person as yet; his name had appeared on the lists her mother had sometimes sent her of guests at a reception; his name was on her visiting list, and she would have to ask him to parties herself in the future. She listened, and admired his speaking voice, it was so much lower and rounder than the usual modern man's. 'I mistrust falsetto voices; they mean weakness, when they don't mean worse,' she had said to herself in the days when she had been accustomed to sum up everything with great promptitude; the days before she was three-and-twenty.

His voice was not the only good thing about Mark to strike a girl's fancy; there was a firmness and a faint pinkness about his face which did not suggest a London life in any way, and yet would have been too delicate for a countryman. His eyes were bright and clear – those curious ringed eyes of grey and hazel; his teeth were perfect; not too small, and very white. Gallia saw all these things rather as a dealer might notice the points in a horse than as a lady might perceive a young man's claims to handsomeness.

'And you are so good as to think my moment has come?' he was saying, smilingly, to Mrs Leighton, and Gallia watched thoughtfully all the time.

'Your moment for what?' she suddenly inquired, and her uncompromising eyes fixed themselves upon him when he turned to her.

'My moment to emerge from the covert of mediocrity into the open of – what shall we say?'

'Predestination,' said Mrs Leighton, with a touch of solemnity under her smile.

'You are going in for public life?' said Gallia, taking a quite impersonal interest in the subject.

'It is the only thing for me to attempt. When a man has no position – no private position of any kind, I mean – and no duties, except towards himself, he had better be trying to succeed, don't you think, in something? It employs his leisure,' Mark replied genially.

'Oh, if he has no interest in outside things – in agriculture, or literature, or art – I suppose he may as well –'

'Be his own field, and book, and marble, Miss Hamesthwaite? I think he may. And it has the merit of being exceedingly difficult,' he went on, with his well-calculated indifference, and a smile that had the curves of satire. 'To some men, success and advancement is, as Mrs Leighton has said, predestined. But my education was not of the right kind; it was scattered and varied.'

'It has made you a man of the world,' Mrs Leighton put in briskly.

'But not of the world of public service,' said Mark, with a shake of his head. 'I ought to have been at Eton; whereas I wasted three or four years at a great public school, learned nothing, and had to do without the *kudos* as well. At Eton a man gets known by his Christian name, if he gets nothing else – or, better still, by a diminutive of his Christian name – and it is all that he requires. You will not believe, Miss Hamesthwaite,' with a dry, whimsical smile upon his face, 'what a difference it makes to a man's career. To have been "Eddy" – better still, to have been "Bobsy" – at Eton, is a guarantce of place and progress! But,' with a glance of deprecation, 'your sympathy encourages one too much. It is a long subject, and I must pray forgiveness for talking so much about myself.' He looked at Mrs Leighton, but turned a glance finally on Gallia. He was not sure if she were despising him for his determination to make something of himself; but he was patient, and he felt that she would not despise him when she knew him better. Mark had discovered that there is no kind of woman who will not admire personal ambition in a man – irrespective of the object of that ambition. Women, Mark knew, will respect a clever murderer if he shows sufficient dexterity. Her next remark, therefore, surprised him, simply spoken though it was.

'The desire to "get on", as it is called, is something I have never been able to comprehend,' she said. Then she turned to her aunt: 'I have forgotten to say till now that papa is coming to dinner tonight, if you are not engaged.'

'That is very charming of him. I quite wondered when we were to meet again, as I go to Aix on Thursday. Are you coming too, dear ? Do. I will make Mr Gurdon stay to entertain you, and we can all go on to Holland House* together. Yes?'

'Thank you, Aunt Celia, but I hadn't intended going to Holland House.' Gurdon had murmured that he would be delighted.

'My dear child, we must have you go about a very little. It is time now that you appeared in some places. You can be quiet without being immured.'

Gallia apparently gave in.

'Then I will go and tell papa: he is at the House of Lords – I may just catch him.'

Gurdon thought the little movement of *au revoir* that she made, and her slow step to the door he was holding, very beautiful in their way. He was quite satisfied to have met her at last. She was driven to Westminster, and sent in a tiny note with the evening plans in it; then with an idle whim she alighted at Dean's Yard and sent her carriage to wait beside her father's.

She liked this old, strange part of London, so unlike London as it is; she liked to wander in the precincts of the Abbey, and look up at the dull red-brick houses, which seemed so comfortable, which seemed to mean something quite apart from all the other buildings in all the great City. It was long since she had strolled into the cloisters, and it would be cool there this hot June day. She took her way past the constable, to that passage, flagged and grey, where mysterious dull-red doors have the air of closing the burrows of canons and other cobwebby and unreal dignitaries. She turned aside into the little court that opens on the left. Did big London know that such a place was in existence? Surely not, or it would tear brick from brick, cast the heavy, time-eaten, wrought ironwork of lamp and sconce and knocker into its metropolitan dust-heap.

She went on, past more red doors, down the long passage to the small, square, grass-centred Court; the air, that had smelt of stone and bone, and lime and time, grew fresher here; the patterns of the tracery in the arches were touched in places by the sun; it was light again – for the open air came there. Gallia, who had not a tear for human ill or sorrow, turned back into the dim flagged passage with her handkerchief to her eyes; she had suddenly grown conscious, as human beings do at times, of the disposition to peace, beauty, dignity, and spiritual loveliness about some places – and it marks the contrast to man and his fret and unrest. Some such dim sense of discord and disparity with a beautiful world had touched Gallia – she stopped, where a shaft of sunlight from the little Court invaded the cloister for a few feet.

'Quite a Royal Academy success,' said a voice behind her, and she looked up, startled, to perceive Mr Essex.

'How are you? You'd be a boon to some struggling fellow who couldn't get in; you'd be the picture of the year.'

Chapter Twenty

In the moment of shaking hands, Gallia discovered a strange thing; her feelings for Essex had undergone some change. She looked quietly into his face, with some idea, perhaps, of seeing whether his glance had any effect upon her; it had an effect, but the effect was different. The thing amounted to this: she had grown, her mind had grown, and she had arranged a scheme of life for herself, had arranged a series of ideas, in none of which Essex could have the least part. Essex, the Essex she had loved, could not touch her now in the same way; the part of her that he had touched and had hurt was atrophied. So much the better or so much the worse for Gallia.

'I had forgotten about you,' she said, in faint surprise at herself.

'Really? But why not?' he asked lightly; 'though I had not quite forgotten you.'

She did not take up this cue.

'What are you doing now?' she enquired.

'Just now I am looking at your hat; a moment since I was wondering how you came here. *You* can't have been calling on an old college friend?'

'For one thing, I have no old college friend to call on. If you know men who live here, can you tell me if this environment affects them in any way? I should change my whole mind if I lived here.'

Essex looked at her whimsically.

'Am I to understand that, not having lived here, you have not changed your mind, and that –'

She interrupted him, again with the same half curious, half surprised, but very quiet expression.

'You need not go so far out of your way to understand or

misunderstand me. Come here and sit down for a moment – I want to see how you make me feel.'

'I can give you a quarter of an hour,' he answered, after a glance at his watch.

'I shan't rob you of all that. Where were you last December?'

'December? – I was in Oxford.'

'I was in Algiers with my mother, and she died at the end of the month. That was when I last thought of you seriously. Then – how odd it seems! – I would have liked so much to see you.'

'Why didn't you telegraph?'

'You needn't say that sort of thing! I am quite aware that I seem a very strange style of person to you, but, you see, to you I say exactly what I mean; when one has once been frank at a very big moment, it seems foolish to be terrified of the effect of little bits of frankness in quite small moments. So I asked you where you were, because I wondered if I came into your mind at all when I was wanting to see you so much.'

'So far as I can recollect, not less or more than usual.'

Gallia laughed – an unamused, unmerry sort of laugh it was.

'And is the world beginning to grow accustomed to the measure of honesty you decided to mete out to it?' Essex asked pleasantly.

'I have, just at present, very little to do with the world. One has not to mind being thought peculiar by a number of people; it doesn't break the skin, that I know of.'

'If adverse opinion took the form of what I believe is called "chaps", how raw we should all be,' remarked Essex. 'And I suppose,' he went on, with an enquiring air, 'it is absolutely impossible to a woman of your nature to let things slide, and be happy, and look pretty, and marry, and love, and bring up children, and work out an amiable, not too complicated or fatiguing, sort of destiny?'

'I certainly hope to bring up a child. I think it is all I do want,' Gallia answered.

'But the other things you cannot give way to?'

'I am as happy as anyone when I see cause. A sail, a good gallop, a day's shooting, will often – in fact, will always make me happy; that's because I'm young and strong, and my blood moves. I do not comprehend the emotional kind of happiness to be got out of some man's admiration of me – or whatever it is that gives it to women. Love did not seem to me a happy thing. It attacked my pride, my independence, the whole fabric of my character; it lowered my crest – I think you might have seen?' She turned to smile at him.

'You still think that you loved me?' Essex asked, almost quite naturally.

'We needn't go into it again; but whatever my feelings may be, and however ill-regulated and untimely, I don't mistake them. I told you that I loved you, and you know why I told you. I wish it had not been necessary, God knows, but you made it necessary.'

He turned fully towards her, leaning his back into the corner of the stone seat and holding his knee with both hands.

'Gallia, I am terribly sorry for you. Don't mistake me; it is nothing to do with your having loved or not having loved me. It is simply because you are the perfectly hapless kind of modern woman. Your whole make-up is an egregious mistake – a complete waste of material. There is no place in all the world for you. You are not wanted, because you are for no use.'

'The earwig of humanity,' she interjected, with a wistful kind of smile.

'You have a beautiful face,' continued Essex, speaking with unusual *entrain*.* 'Good heavens, child, what eyes you have! And what use are those eyes to you ? They are shaped to look things of which you have no knowledge. Your lips – one could imagine, if one saw a picture of you, the most emotional moments in the world made by your lips. And you use them – good Lord! – you use them to talk the flimsiest philosophy – the sociology of a schoolgirl's half-holiday!'

Gallia's face was quite grave, was sometimes sad, but a light was growing at the back of her eyes, the light she had gleaned since she saw Essex last.

'Physically you are so lovely,' he went on in a more argumen-tative key, 'that one regrets you have no grain of coquetry to make play with all these bodily gifts, even if it were cruel play. I think – do you know this? – I think that when I made some sort of love to you at Mrs Leighton's, I was only misled by your appearance into thinking you the sort of woman that you looked. You are not heartless in the way of being cold and indifferent – that has gone out with women now – you are simply incapable of an ordinary feminine feeling.' Essex had no idea that this was said with a strong note of irritation, of resentment. 'As I look at you now, you are the sort of being an amorous-minded man, which you know I am not, would sell his whole career to kiss. It is your outward form that looks so; it does not suit your mind; it will give you trouble yet, for men will fall in love with it. That will not be your fault, but the bitterness will be all yours. For you are a misshapen woman.'

Gallia heard all this with very little surprise, it was not so new to her; and though she felt the touch of scorn in Essex's voice, she knew the scorn was not his, but was his outraged sex speaking in him. When he applied his last epithet to her, she never winced.

'But there is something more than love in the world, is there not?' Her voice was a whisper, an anxious whisper.

'For women? Nothing! What else should there be?'

'There is motherhood.' This time her voice was calm, only her eyes looked wistfully before her.

Essex looked a little more curiously at her.

'A mad anomaly!' he exclaimed.

'One should be beautifully made and beautiful to be a mother,' she said again, still staring wistfully before her. 'Perhaps' – she seemed to recollect him and turned towards him with a half-hearted smile and her eyes magnified by the tears in them – 'perhaps there is a bigger object in my appearance than the satisfaction of any man's senses.'

'Good heavens, what a coil! Then you have some sort of feelings?' He was genuinely surprised.

'Listen,' Gallia said. 'At any rate one can talk to you and – you – don't gasp. Listen. The first sort of love, the amorous love, is over and done in me. I hadn't a seam or a big vein of it.

I think I had only a "pocket" – and it's worked out; wouldn't pay to sink another shaft for that. The capacity for mother-love, I think, is very large in me; I think I should make a good mother: I can't tell you how I know, but I have been finding it out ever since my own mother died, and I began to know it when I sat beside her dead body. I could spend myself and lose myself in my child, if I had one, and ask for no return; for everything else *I* come first; but I shouldn't come first there. When I marry, I shall, of course, marry without love. For that is used up. It is my misfortune, and has come out of the crookedness of things, that I didn't love the right person at the right time.'

Essex was looking at her with more of himself in his eyes than anyone had ever seen there before. When her voice dropped, an impulse taught him to take her hand. He took it, but she did not appear to notice him or his action. She was just talking out her soul to the grey stones, softened oddly by their influence, and also because she was beside the only human being who understood her.

'But that has nothing to do with the rest. On the whole, it may be an advantage. If I were to fall in love again, it might be with someone quite unsuitable to be the father of my child – someone who would not be fine and strong and healthy, and of a healthy stock. As it is, when I marry – I talk of it quite as a certainty because it is a certainty to me, being rich and good-looking, and the only child of my father – I shall marry solely with a view to the child I am going to live for.' She turned towards him again in a rising tumult of feeling, and clasped the hand he had given her in both hers. They were trembling a little, he noticed, but though he felt some strong emotion himself, he concealed it bravely, for he knew it had nothing in common with the emotion she felt. 'So don't you think – don't you think that there may be a place in the world for me after all?'

At the moment she had told her love for him, she had left him cold and normal; now, describing a greater and more spiritual feeling, she lit strange fires. Two passers-by went down the cloister passage at this moment, men hurrying along; oddly enough, they did not observe the pair sitting on the seat, hand

held in hand. It gave Essex a moment to control himself, to fold
his lip and batten down some flame that would have been half
articulate only. Then he kissed both her hands with a quietness
that came natural to him at this moment of passionate feeling,
he even laid them for a moment upon his breast, then, still
holding them, looked into her eyes.

'I am not making love to you now, Beautiful, Beautiful . . .'
he said, very, very low; then, having told this momentous lie for
her sake, he kissed the hands once more and put them down.

'I know you are not,' she said simply. 'You have heard, and
you know – for you said it yourself – I am not the sort of
woman to be made love to.' Essex's lips twitched uneasily once
or twice in something that was not unlike a smile. 'But I need
not be cut down like the green fig-tree* on that account, for I
may be of some use after all; there must always be room in the
world for a good mother of children, and I will teach them none
of the unhappy things I know when I bring them up.'

'Gallia,' Essex began hesitatingly, and moving a little closer
to her, 'have you thought – with that odd clear head of yours –
about the thing you propose?'

'Motherhood? Often and often. I am very strong, and I have
never known what it is to be frightened at anything. I am not
frightened.'

'Not motherhood,' he said, still speaking low and with his
dark eyes curiously intent upon her face. 'Marriage without
love.'

Gallia was silent a moment; then she nodded her head 'The
same answer as before,' she said.

'Because there would be years of it; and marriage is not' –
Essex would have roared with laughter at this stupendous phrase
if he had heard it in cold blood – 'is not all motherhood.' But
the strength of the whole moment was that Essex's cold blood
was hot.

'Other women bear the same sort of thing.'

'They have married for money or position, and they have
reckoned on the price all along.'

'Ah, but *other* women, who have very little money and no

position; who have often a difficulty to get a living; women who are not married. My position will be just this much better than theirs, that I shall be a mother.' The triumph in her voice was somehow pitiful.

He shivered a little.

'They are not bred as you are, they haven't your feelings.'

'Why not? Some of them must be well bred; and just now you said I hadn't any feelings!'

'I never said you had no feelings of delicacy or refinement,' Essex replied, with quick severity.

'It does not seem to me,' she spoke cynically and coldly, 'judging merely by pathological facts such as come under everyone's notice, that marriage can have much to do with delicacy and refinement.'

He shook his head.

'My dear, you are becoming the modern woman again, and a moment since you were primary – and exquisite.'

'Well, we'll put that aside. Of course,' lowering her tone and making it hard and crisp, 'I quite know it, if I were differently made, I might dread it; but I look at it like the women who marry for position and money – as a price. It is a pity, as I heard a girl say the other day, that it is not an affair of "money down" – that one cannot write a big cheque, and be done. But these things are the inherent disadvantages that cannot be done away with. And it leaves me very clear in mind. To be marrying for love might bring about one's object less satisfactorily. If I were living fifty years hence, I should not probably have to marry at all. But our yoke is the ignorance of our day. Dark, I have talked enough. I am going now.' She stood up. He remained seated, thinking. It was a beautiful deep twilight in the cloister now.

'How is it you have talked so inwardly to me?' he asked, with a shadow in his eyes.

'Because with you I have no *mauvaise honte*.* How should I have ? Did I not take the very widest step that afternoon in my room last year?' She seemed quite free and simple with him, but there was a warm colour in her cheek and a light in her eyes. If his life had depended on it, Essex could not have prevented the words that rose in him, or stemmed the flood that brought them.

'Was it true then – what you said?' he asked, in a low voice that he kept even with difficulty.

'Quite true then.'

'Then.' He repeated the word gravely. His head was bent, his face hidden. He stood up beside her. 'And now I cannot bear to think of how cruel I was to you. How brutal!' He put his arms round her shoulders. 'May I kiss you and be forgiven? The man you loved, who is to be the only man you love, may kiss you now? It is quiet here, but all the world might be present for me.' His voice rocked unevenly for a moment, but he steadied himself, and Gallia's eyes fed on his excitement. 'How cold you found me! We suffer for the degeneracy of our day. But I have enough passion' – his voice broke in a note like laughter – 'to kiss you once.' He threw back his head when his lips left hers. 'Love, love! My love – love,' he said, and the word, which feeling made sing in the air, had that in it which seemed to cradle Gallia's heart; she leaned and rested on these tones, tasting something of the peace of sleep. Then his head bent forward, and she felt its weight upon her own, the curve of his cheek was against her forehead. Quick to learn and to respond, this new moment was teaching her fast, but he raised his head and said, 'You will know that for half an hour you were worshipped, for a minute you were kissed . . . and . . .'

She looked up at him with the only look of its kind her face ever wore, then she turned and walked away towards the gate.

In the odd harmony that had come to be between them, Gallia was conscious of some strange chord that sounded curiously. That Essex was sincere, for the first time in his life perhaps, she felt, and that was enough.

She could not know the inside of this man's mind, nor tell that the odd chord was Essex's own amazement at himself. The man was finding another self. For years he had sown and reaped in the home pastures of his soul, but, straying vaguely to an unsought hill-top, had unwittingly climbed the ridge and set foot in an undiscovered country.*

Chapter Twenty-One

Essex, leaving the cloister, now dimly lamplit, some hour or so after Gallia flitted away, came across a friend and dined with him at the House of Commons, and was during dinner, as the friend was fain to remark, even more himself than usual. Then, having walked up and down the terrace till half-past ten, he said good-night, and took his way on foot to Hammersmith. Some men believe greatly in the calming effects of long walks, though what calm does a tiger find, who pads almost ceaselessly the length of his cage? During the dinner and the after-talk, Essex had not once thought of Gallia; no sooner, however, was he striding through the network of Belgravian streets, than his mind seemed to pick up the turmoil of his thoughts just where he had dropped them when Shale clapped him on the shoulder.

What proved – had not everything in his whole character proved previously – that Essex was a man of the least possible emotional experience, was the fact that he was surprised when his memory failed to give back a detailed and phonographed replica of his and Gallia's conversation. He remembered a number of isolated sentences that had fallen from her lips, but what, he wondered, had been his answers to them? Were such subjects as these ever contemplated by the religious-minded, his aberrations might be alluded to as a merciful dispensation. No truthfully recorded conversation of the highly emotional kind could fail to sound ridiculous, were one to observe it with a frigid or even with a tepid mind. Slightly warmed and relaxed the mind must be to judge such matter. (It is fortunate that the people whose opinions matter, have only time to read novels in the evening, or late at night.) The finest love-scenes ever written are those that can be read at eleven A.M., without sounding sickly or silly.

To a cynic such as Essex, with a thinness of skin like his in
the matter of seeming absurd, the details of that half-hour in the
cloisters would have appeared farcical indeed. But all that
remained to him was a confused memory; a memory startling,
but puzzling, pleasurable. That he should have acted as he had
done surprised Essex, but it did not disconcert him; no, not
though it seemed so unusual and astonishing; he remained fully
satisfied with himself. That some people might perceive an
indelicacy in kissing and professing to love a lady to whom he
had no idea of offering marriage, Essex was unaware, or if he
were aware, would have waived as trivial. Besides, he knew that
in Gallia's mind, as in the minds of many other thoughtful
people, love and marriage were regarded as justly separate. He
knew Gallia had understood him; he was sure – and he was
quite right in being sure – that he had left her a sense of
satisfaction, of fulfilment. She would proceed on her way, he on
his, and they walk to their separate destinies.

As he passed down Kensington, he saw the long line of
carriages going up to Holland House; but he had not Mark
Gurdon's acquaintance with people's crests and arms and liver-
ies, and, having no psychic sense, he was quite unaware that
Gallia, more lovely than ever before, was sitting beside Mrs
Leighton in one of those carriages, and that her father and Mark
Gurdon were seated opposite to her.

Love is a very short, small, and frequently unimportant
incident in the lives of most people. It is meant to be. If the days
of a man's life be threescore years and ten, during which he gets
up and goes to bed between the performance of stupid but
necessary duties, it is only reasonable that at the most he should
offer up a sacrifice of six months or so to love. The Honourable
Gallia Hamesthwaite, unphotographed, unparagraphed, and
ungossiped about, passed in the plenitude of her beauty from
room to room; kinder, more tolerant of stupidity than usual;
more gracious and more approachable, but with a superbness
about her that is only to be seen in the face and manner of a
woman who has picked her aloe-flower.*

Mark Gurdon was often beside her; Mrs Leighton observed

and admired and approved her, and, clever old lady as she was, never suspected Mark's dawning ambition. Whether it woke definitely then, or whether he had felt thrills of it before, cannot be told. But he was annoyed to think, when he shut their carriage door upon the ladies, that he had thought of going to Edwards Square that night, since he was in the neighbourhood, and had not seen Cara for two or three days. He walked briskly to Edwards Square, his face flushing and his eye kindling with thought induced by the scene he had left, not the scene he was going to. What we call delicacy is a quality wholly unknown to Life and Nature; Nature has no regard for the fitness of things, and Life arranges the most tasteless contrasts. For instance, it was far from agreeable of them both to make Gallia attract Mark with the light lit by Essex's kisses, and it was equally *outré* in them to send Mark to the arms of his mistress with his head filled with thoughts of another woman. But none of the persons concerned were to blame for these contingencies. Life and Nature were alone responsible, and can only be excused on the ground that neither is really well-bred.

The studio was lighted when he knocked, and a step which was not Cara's came towards the door. It was opened by the charwoman who had befriended Cara when her father met with his accident and when she met with Gurdon; the woman now came daily to do what service she required.

'She's very bad, poor dear,' said Mrs Miles, in a voice of deep sympathy; and Mark's face, which a moment before had been fired by ambition, fell hastily to lines of genuine anxiety.

'Ill? How? Since when?'

Without waiting for an answer, he pushed past the *portière*, and came swiftly to the broad couch on which, among a number of bright cushions and rugs, he saw the girl's pale face.

She was awake and knew him, though her first words showed her mind was wandering. In an instant Mark's cloak was off, and he was kneeling beside her, raising up her head and putting the wild-looking hair out of her eyes.

'Whatever she would 'a done if it hadn't of been my day a' comin', God knows,' said the woman fervently.

'But have you done anything? Have you sent for a doctor? When was she taken ill? Did you find her so?'

Mrs Miles posed herself, with her arms wrapped across the strings of her three aprons.

'Hight o'clock is my hour a' comin', which I 'ave to git Miles's breakfuss before 'e goes hout of a mornin'. I 'adn't got down our court before I says, "There, I've forgot the baskit," it came over me all of a minute, and there, I says, "Little miss 'll never 'eed if I'm a minit late," for punckchell's been my motter since hiver I took to charin', which was wen Miles took to drink –'

'But when you got here, my good woman, when you got here – was she ill?'

'Wen I 'ad the baskit, sir,' Mrs Miles continued, with an air of one who rigidly adheres to truth, and will not step aside for anything – 'Wen I 'ad the baskit, I came on in a 'urry, and come hup to the door, sir, same as you might, that unthinkin'.'

'And I was dancing – dancing,' Cara was saying in a low whisper, and playing upon the covering with her fingers, as though in imitation of the figure of a dance.

'Which she wasn't, sir, for knock and knock I did, and then at last I 'eard a groan. Aoh!' Mrs Miles placed one hand below her waist and just in front of the ample curve of her hip. 'I don' know as ever I came over the same since I was carryin' Hemmer; which I was took so I couldn't kerry a bucket, not the shillin' size, and Miles 'ad to borrer off the landlord of the "King o' Denmark", which he wouldn't lend him more than fourpence in the shillin' on 'is score.'

With a patience that did him credit, Gurdon forbore to interrupt Mrs Miles again; he employed himself in very gently straightening the rugs and covers and cushions of the lounge, and making the poor soul more comfortable; but he was ready, on the instant that Mrs Miles should reach the kernel of the story, to leap up and fetch a doctor.

'An' I 'eard a sound,' continued the good woman, who had detailed at least one family reminiscence in the meantime which Mark's ear had failed to catch, 'like you was polishin' one of them parky floors with a clawth, an', aoh my! it was 'er a-draggin' 'erself along the wall and floor to hopin the door.'

'What did she say to you?' put in Mark sharply.

'Say? She was pas' speakin', and took 'er up in my arms I did, and kerry her in 'ere on the sofa. She's been talkin' a deal of furrin talk, but wen I undress her I soon give a guess wot was up, pore young woman – not but wot I've 'eard these furrin natures 'as it easier, but I did wot I could, and got 'ot water and give 'er fermentations same as the doctor hordered me, an' made all neat, for it's a hawkward spot with illness –'

'Have you had a doctor?' Mark broke in, feeling his brain turning with Miles's chatter.

The woman looked at him rather sharply, and her expression, as he afterwards recalled it, puzzled him greatly.

'I didn't know wot might be your wish, sir; an' I done wot I could, bein' accustom' to illness; there's beef-tea a-makin' now, and give 'er beefjelly, wot I run to the chemiss for, and was obliged to take 'er purse, but you'll see as one and ninepence was every bit I took, sir. It's strengthening stuff she needs and careful nursin', but then I can't leave Miles, 'e do drink that shockin' wen I'm away, and negleck 'is family something shameful, still I could stay most of the time and run 'ome hivery now and then if you was willing.'

'Thank you,' Mark said, gladly accepting as kindness what was probably merely the avid relish of illness common to her class. 'But I will have a doctor now, and if you can come every day, I will nurse her myself all night. The first thing to do is to find out what is the matter.' A sharp look from the faded eye of Mrs Miles was lost upon him. 'What, dear?' bending over Cara; 'you were dancing? And did you fall? And why were you dancing so much?' His voice was very tender indeed, and his face kind and gentle as he looked at her.

A look of intelligence came into her eyes. 'I was frightened, and so I thought I would dance and dance . . .'

He shook his head vaguely.

'Bein' no stairs to come up and down,' said Mrs Miles in a

furtive undertone, and glancing round the building in a depre-
catory manner.

'Stay by her and watch her, and I will fetch a doctor,' said
Mark, getting up. 'Or no, better you go – you will know the
neighbourhood; I will stay and look after her. Tell him to come
at once.'

'There's two in the Square, but perhaps you wouldn't wish –'

'Either of them; whichever is youngest and will come out
quickest: it must be past two o'clock. And you need not come
back.'

He shut the door after her carefully, and then came back to
walk to and fro in the room with a puzzled face. Once he
stopped to open the big skylight, through which the pale June
stars looked very far off. Gurdon was a humane man, although
he had had few opportunities of making the discovery. He was
now much disturbed in mind, and with strange accesses of
unselfish kindliness assailing him. He looked frequently at
Cara's flushed face and tossed hair; sometimes he stopped and
smoothed her forehead with his hand, but for the most part he
strode up and down quickly and silently, his black evening shoes
making no noise upon the boards and rugs of the studio.

Three-quarters of an hour passed before the brisk step of a
man outside announced the arrival of a doctor, hurried and a
trifle irritable, as a man might well be who had gone to bed at
twelve, after a long day, and been roused at 2.30 from his
deepest sleep.

He looked sharply at Mark and his evening dress, and
appeared to think someone else would come forward to explain
what had occurred, and what was wanted.

Mrs Miles had gone home, and the burden of the situation
was with Mark. The doctor's manner and the nature of his
questions caused him some embarrassment, but the seriousness
of the interview made him forget it again.

He could give very little information about the illness, and the
doctor had to be contented with the fact that Mrs Miles would
give a full account in the morning. But Mark held the lamp

while Dr Hudson made a hurried examination, and waited eagerly for the temperature to be mentioned.

'She will do nicely if this fever can be kept down: I will send you something at once to fight that; there is a messenger call at my house in the Square, and several all-night chemists. Inconvenient? Oh, she might be in many a worse place. Plenty of good air here, and the quietest spot in London.' He began to write a prescription on a leaf of his pocket-book. 'You say you can get someone to look after her at night. Very well; but I will send in a nurse first thing in the morning, with your permission, to attend to the patient and prepare her for my visit about ten. No, we can do nothing more now, save keep up the strength a little and get the temperature down. Tomorrow I shall be able to make a definite statement about the cause of trouble.' He looked up, this keen, worldly-wise young man, and met Mark's still rather puzzled eyes. 'I have no doubt I am leaving the patient in the most careful hands, meanwhile. Good-night.'

When he had gone, Mark sat down by Cara in the empty, quiet studio, and looked long at her little face, pale again now with a fine saffron pallor. 'Poor little thing, I suppose you owe this to me,' he said.

Chapter Twenty-Two

During the fortnight that followed the party at Holland House, Gallia had been rather busy socially.

A number of her mother's old friends, people whom she knew only in the traditional family way, sent invitations of a quiet kind to her; almost every day she seemed to be lunching with someone, and she appeared at a number of the fashionable afternoon concerts. In the mornings, after her ride, she more than once secured Margaret to do some shopping with her, and in the course of time a silvery grey and white plumage replaced the black of her earlier mourning months. Then suddenly Lord Hamesthwaite decided to make an immediate move to the Hall, and some housemaids were despatched to help the permanent staff of servants there to be ready earlier for the coming of the family.

Mrs Essex and Margaret had to be prevailed upon to come sooner, for Gallia had no desire to be left alone in the country. She had appeared to fall in with her father's idea, and there was to be a constant succession of guests throughout the summer, since she refused to go abroad.

Mrs Leighton, immersed in the formalities of the cure at Aix, was feeling astonishingly miserable.

'I am not sure that I have ever been so ill as during the first week at this atrocious place. I should leave immediately if I were not too prostrate to travel. How infinitely preferable a nice English attack of rheumatism would be. But I needn't distress you with the wails of a tiresome old woman, particularly when I have something quite important to say, and the pains in my right arm threaten to prevent all correspondence. This, then, dear Gallia, is what troubles me. Robbie is coming home. He has not dared to write to your father since the dreadful letter he received about two months ago, the result, I have always been convinced, of an entire misconception. Spain still seems to be a very difficult country to travel in, especially when one leaves the beaten track, as Robbie in his adventurous way naturally hastened to do. He gives me the entire explanation of the gambling episode; and you will remember I endeavoured to assure your father at the time that he was taking too severe a view altogether. It seems that Robbie had engaged a mule, and packed all the delightful draperies and embroideries he had secured upon the beast, as well as his luggage, containing, foolish boy, his reserve sum of money. At the end of an exhausting journey across the mountains, he drove this beast into a stable, and actually in the time that he was eating a most unsavoury meal, the animal and all the baggage disappeared, stolen, of course. He wasted about a week in fruitless endeavours to secure the attention of the authorities, and it was *only then*, when he was at his last penny, that he gambled for *pesetas* – for his dinner really, poor boy – in the low inns and among the gipsies. I want you to have him at the Hall at once, if you can; you will find him full of delightful stories, and you will persuade your father to be more lenient to him than he has been before. If we back him up, he says he will have no difficulty in establishing himself in London, now that his course of study is over.'

That merely made one more for Gallia's little house-party, and she remembered Robbie as an engaging, open-natured, happy-minded fellow, who would be a certain acquisition in any country house.

She came down the staircase from her own rooms after reading Mrs Leighton's letter, dressed for going out. In the passages and on the landing were plenty of signs of a hurried flitting. The servants were at work rolling up carpets and taking down curtains, and making other preparations in view of the house being closed for three or four months. The mechanism of housekeeping was a dead letter to Gallia; she had no idea of the time and trouble, the myriads of small duties, that go towards managing a house. If she had known, she would have been filled with a very wholesome and active contempt for half of the accepted *formulae*; she would have instituted a sweeping simplification.

Just at that moment, passing down the stairs, her eye fell on a soft-headed brush with a brass attachment in the middle of its abnormally long handle, and a wonder as to its use seized her suddenly, and she paused in idle irony with her hand on the balustrade.

At that moment came a crash, a cry, and some detached screams, from behind one of the big white drawing-room doors. She hurried into the room, and her appearance seemed to add to the confusion of the knot of maid-servants gathered round a fallen step-ladder, opposite one of the four windows. A heap of pale yellow silk damask mixed up with the latter suggested immediately that a servant had fallen while taking down a curtain. As the window was some twelve feet high, there was the material for a very pretty accident, and Gallia crossed the room at her swiftest pace to see what was amiss.

'Which of you is hurt?' she demanded of the astonished group, two of whom were on the floor supporting an older woman, and one mechanically gathering up the curtain, and seeming to examine it for possible damage.

'Never mind the curtain, Emily. What is this? Who has been hurt?'

'I don't know if the ladder could give way, miss, or if she overbalanced herself,' the maid began. 'I didn't see it myself,' she went on, with the usual haste of a domestic to clear herself in view of possible blame; 'I was over at the mantelpiece moving the corner-pieces.'

'It's the charwoman, miss, that was on the ladder,' broke in Fraser, the second housemaid, 'and I think it must have been in reaching up too high above her head. I told her to go up a step more and she'd have been more at her ease.'

'You told her? How could you do such a wicked, lazy thing? You were too idle or too frightened to go up yourselves, and so you sent an old woman up to do your work. I am ashamed to have such women in my service. Emily, go for Mrs Bostock at once.'

The words fell slowly and coldly from the dispassionate Gallia. Very seldom indeed had she occasion to address any of her servants, with the exception of her own footman and her maid. She was held in the awe with which all servants regard a mistress who is habitually unconscious of their existence.

The girls flushed hotly at her reprimand, but did not dare to offer any excuse. Gallia took the place of one of them beside the injured charwoman, and in a few minutes Mrs Bostock, the housekeeper, arrived.

'I think we must have a mattress and carry her to the nearest bedroom; I fear it is serious.'

It was wonderful how quickly the poor soul was carried to a bachelor bedroom on the same landing, by the now eager servants, reinforced by the footman; but it was Gallia's own hand that applied the restoratives and brought back groaning consciousness to the sufferer.

Mrs Bostock had left the room with a maid on a search for different bedding; Emily had borne a message to the carriage which was awaiting Gallia, and now drove off for a doctor; and Fraser, as principal culprit, had escaped to a more sympathetic *milieu* in the servants' hall. Gallia was alone when the charwoman came to her senses.

'It's my side, m'm – my lady – an' my back. Oh lor! oh dear! My back struck the floor and the ladder come a-top of me; I 'ope I 'aven't broke my column! But it's my side as feels the wrinch; it never 'as been right since a fall I 'ad in our mews when I was going with Johnnie; stipped on the cat, I did, a nasty little sandy cat Miles kep' in the stable – 'e was drivin' for Serumfry Paget then. Oo – ooh!'

'Yes; now lie still for a minute, and first drink some of this. When you feel a little stronger, we will get your clothes off.'

'Thank you, my lady. It is a gnoring pain just above the 'ip joint, an' –'

'Now pray be silent, or you will exhaust your strength, and won't be able to tell the doctor how you feel,' Gallia said, in her firm, quiet voice. The effect of this remonstrance lasted several minutes, no doubt by virtue of the last touch, which appealed strangely to Mrs Miles's pride of ailment.

It was Gallia who assisted her own maid to undress Mrs Miles; it seemed to her the Frenchwoman's hands moved fussily about the task.

'Six years have I come in an' out this house, and nothink never happened,' Mrs Miles maundered on in an undertone. ''Twas me as took down the drawing-rooms when they was cherry and cream – cherry and cream with gold galoon, 'ung in panels, they was –'

'Can you bear me to turn you just a little, to unfasten your skirt? That will do. Now, then, just a moment – yes, I am sure it pains you, but you will feel better when they are off.'

With that tender firmness which some women have by nature, some others learn in the hospitals, and most never learn at all, Gallia removed the poor outer clothing, multifarious in strings and pins. Further than this she hesitated at first to go: would the poor thing feel more uncomfortable to have a lady or a servant made familiar with her shifts and makeshifts? Gallia's good sense decided for her, and she proceeded with her task.

'Me lyin' here,' began the woman, in a more excited key, 'and poor Missie with no one to 'ot 'er beef-tea for 'er, nurse bein' out, for I promis' to run in at dinner-time, it's only ten minutes in the bus!'

'What are you anxious about? Do you wish a message sent to your home? That will be easily done; I will call Emily, and you shall tell her –'

'Oh, it isn't that, my lady. Oo – ooh!'

'Bear up a little longer; see, take another drink of this. There. I shan't take off the bodice, just loosen it upon your chest a little.'

An instinct taught Gallia that small soothing sentences, at short intervals, kept the patient's attention from her hurt.

'Never mind,' as something slipped to the floor from Mrs Miles's shawl-spread bosom; 'it's only a letter, I'll put it on the mantelpiece –'

'Oh dearie dear, whatever shall I do?' the poor creature wailed suddenly. 'Missie told me to be sure and send it! I had to put it in the pillar before twelve, so as 'e'd have it early this afternoon.'

'Make yourself quite easy about it! Ah, I hear the doctor coming! I shall give orders for you to be well looked after, and shall be back in two hours to see you myself. The letter? It shall be sent at once by one of the servants.' Gallia took it hastily, and called a soft 'Come in!'

Mrs Bostock ushered in the doctor, and, after a few words of explanation, Miss Hamesthwaite hurried to the carriage. She was over-due in Hammersmith Terrace, where her mission was to prevail upon the Essexes to hasten their visit to the Hall. In the outer lobby she stopped.

'Knowles, I wish William to take this letter at once to' – she turned it over as she spoke, and her eyes fell on the address. The note was directed to 'Mark Gurdon, Esq., The Colonial Office, Whitehall.' But this was not what surprised Gallia, or convinced her that her own footman had best not deliver it. 'Never mind, Knowles, I shall not require William.'

She got into the carriage, and sat reflecting while Hendon waited for his order.

'Stop at the first boy-messenger office,' she said.

All the way down Kensington Road she kept thinking. Gallia's was a very alert and ready mind, but she was puzzled to think how Mrs Miles should be in possession of a note from a sick person, to whom she referred as 'Missie', which was addressed to Mark Gurdon – in Mark Gurdon's own handwriting.

Chapter Twenty-Three

Two days later, Gallia and her father left for the country, and they left in Lord Hamesthwaite's favourite manner, namely, in their own carriage.

Without being enormously wealthy people, they were decidedly rich, and for a man in his position Lord Hamesthwaite's expenditure was inconsiderable. He could afford, he averred, to sacrifice a pair of carriage-horses every year; for this his coachman never failed to convey to him was what must happen if he insisted upon driving the two weary roans, fat and artificially spirited, over forty miles of Surrey turnpike in the middle of July. A second pair was therefore ordered from the Hall, to be in readiness at Guildford, and, covered with dust, father and daughter duly arrived at their beautiful Surrey home, which had been restored by Gallia's grandfather, and still preserved the quaint charm it had possessed as an old red-brick and timbered manor house.

Those two days had been busy ones for Gallia. She had saddled herself, considering it the barest duty, with the care of the poor charwoman who had been injured in her service, and Mrs Miles was now established in the neighbouring hospital, with two fractured ribs and an easy conscience. For had not Miss Hamesthwaite, than whom no one was more delicately reserved in the matter of befriending and patronising the poor, herself sent down to 'the Mews' and arranged that one pound a week should find its way to the pocket of 'Halice', the thirteen-year offspring of the drunken coachman and the poor hard-worked soul, who had said piteously, and without any sense of its humour, 'If you'll believe me, my lady, I've never 'ad a day's illness nor a day's 'oliday since I was married', – regarding both as equally desirable respites.

These arrangements had not been concluded without a second and even third conversation with Mrs Miles, in which further information regarding Mark Gurdon's connection with 'little Missie,' as well as the illness of the latter, had formed a large part of Mrs Miles's superfluous running commentary. The accident and the attention she was exciting made Mrs Miles more talkative than usual, and she insisted upon choosing Gallia as the recipient of her confidences.

Gallia had no experience in dealing with women of this class – indeed, Miles was the first specimen she had come across – and although she sometimes succeeded in stemming the torrent of wholly irrelevant matter, and always succeeded in greatly impressing the charwoman, she every now and then became inundated and swamped by fresh streams, and acquired perforce much private information concerning the inner life of an acquaintance. Putting aside her annoyance at having learnt certain private facts about a man she knew, the whole thing had, from many aspects and for many reasons, an effect on Gallia's mind.

The day after her arrival at the Hall, no visitors being yet come, she went briskly out to the stables to choose which horse she would ride. She felt the necessity of a long time of thought, and she knew nothing so conducive to it as hours in the saddle by field and fallow, by copse and hill.

The stables were a great feature at the Hall, and Lord Hamesthwaite was, distantly and quite ignorantly, very proud of his horses. For himself, two would have been sufficient; the big white horse he drove in town, and the solid, fiddle-headed* cob he rode in the country.

But with Gallia it was different. Her pair of skewbalds and double dog-cart were known in every village in the Weald; nothing could beat her little Norfolk trotter in the dark-green cart; and her particular pride was a perfectly appointed Devonshire donkey jingle, in which a very fleet dark jackass flipped along the road on pointed hoofs.

This time she rode a half-bred Arab, capable of a ten-mile

canter which bade fair to send its rider to sleep, and took her
way by a bridle-path through a wood of chestnuts.

A smiling morning of perfect summer did not reflect smiles on
Gallia's face. She rode along, wrapped up in her own thoughts,
unconscious of flowers and birds; observing the road before her
and her horse in that accurate but mechanical fashion common
to all good riders. Her face was in its severest mask. She was
paler than usual, owing perhaps to fatigue, perhaps merely to
mental tension. She was searching diligently in her brain for the
reason of a sensation she had experienced. She was perplexed
because it seemed to her she had been guilty of a logical
inconsistency.

The proposition, as she phrased it, was this: she had heard
that Mark Gurdon had a mistress. That was the initial fact. On
hearing this, she had been conscious of strong moral revulsion.
And that was the crux: considering what her own view of the
subject had always been, that put her about.

Why should she experience a sense of nausea on hearing as
much about any man? Why particularly about Gurdon, whom
she had met less than a dozen times, and merely liked with a
liking the most ordinary?

She reflected upon this without any solution occurring to her,
and her manner of reflection was peculiar. Just as she would
have all the world be fair and honest with all the world, so she
was fair and honest with herself. She regarded herself, very
reasonably, as two people – her reason as one person, her
feelings as another. She imagined in her mind a kind of platform
from which first her reason spoke, and, as it were, stepped
down; in the open moment that followed, her feelings made
themselves heard in the same place.

At length it struck her, that until she could discover whether
the fact of a man keeping a mistress would disgust her, should
she hear it of any casual acquaintance, no conclusion could be
come to.

'My feeling is so odd and vague in this matter, that I think it
must be a sort of elemental sex impulse speaking in me, and not
personal feeling at all,' was the leaf of wisdom that floated from

the big tree and fell at length upon the surface of her mind. 'I must put the question to some other girl.' Miss Janion's personality flashed before her, and she smiled – smiled, and then laughed aloud, so that Mahmoud turned one ear backward shiveringly. It would be amusing to have Miss Janion down when Lord Shillinglee and the others came, for instance; but the question should be put to Margaret during the first private talk they had together.

She gathered up her reins, and the light pressure of her leg behind his girth opened Mahmoud like a pair of scissors, and he bounded off for a gallop.

'There is a human soil in human thought of which the oak trees, thank God, know nothing!' Gallia laughed again at the confused feeling she had attempted to put into words, and Mahmoud, taking that as an encouragement, thrashed his feet into the deep summer dust of the road, that stifled the green acorns with white powder.

When she had swallowed sufficient of the tonic of a gallop, Gallia settled her horse to his exquisite Eastern pace. Past a common with necklaces of young geese upon it; then a halt while a gate was deftly opened, Mahmoud breasting it at the instant Gallia's crop loosened the catch; forward again, this time on a wood road, where squirrels and partridges crossed almost beneath the horse's nose; past openings that showed sudden cornfields; past hazel coppices thick with green cobs; past tangles of ripening bramble-berries; past farms and new ricks of hay, smelling stronger, and a thousand times more sweetly, than the corner of Bond Street and Burlington Gardens, till at length, outside the village of Hiddenfold, Gallia drew rein.

'Ah, it is too hot for this,' she said, casting back her open coat and wondering why she had let herself get so hot. 'I shall positively have to see if I can get some lemonade somewhere.'

Mahmoud blew a portentous snuffle, the best sound save a whinny that can be heard from a horse, when Gallia brought up at the door of a little thirteenth-century inn.

As everyone knew Miss Hamesthwaite by sight, attendance to her wants was swift. The homely ginger-pop from a stone bottle

completely refreshed her, and she drank it slowly, unabashed by
the eyes of two dusty cyclists, who, with purple faces and necks
above their grey club clothes, were irrigating lime-choked chan-
nels by means of a quart pot of shandy-gaff.*

Gallia's roving glance penetrated easily to the interior of a
tiny sitting-room on the left of the door, and she was not much
astonished to recognise a friend extended in a long basket chair
in the shade of the window geraniums. At his full length, in cool
grey, a grey crush hat still upon his head, waistcoatless, with a
white silk shirt rising and falling to every breath, lay Dark Essex,
sound asleep. The table was covered with papers and books and
other signs of industry, but the worker, looking amazingly
handsome, lay stretched beside his tools, overcome by the
warmth of the day. Though she had heard he was at 'a little pub
in Surrey', as he had phrased it to his sister, she had not known
that Hiddenfold, only some dozen miles from the Hall, was the
spot he had chosen. Looking round, she did not wonder at his
choice. It was a delicious village.

'I rather wish he were not here,' Gallia said, as she finished
her drink hastily; 'and yet, why not? Why not? On the whole, I
am glad. He is the one person in the world I can talk to.'

With some caution she put Mahmoud on the turf and crossed
the green, rather than risk waking the sleeper by riding past his
window.

Chapter Twenty-Four

The first few days of Margaret's stay were devoted by Gallia to giving her riding-lessons in the park, and driving her about with her mother in the afternoons. Once or twice Gallia had mooted an invitation to Hubert Essex to walk over and lunch, or be driven over to dine, but always Margaret had gently negatived the plan.

'He is so hard at work,' she said; 'if you would like me to be frank, I will say that he would be angry with me for letting you know his whereabouts.'

'That would be very silly of him,' observed Gallia, smiling. 'And, you know, it is possible to refuse an invitation.'

'Of course; but he would think he ought to call, and I don't suppose he has more than one suit here.'

'Men's sense of etiquette – which must proceed from vanity – is a thing I cannot keep pace with,' Gallia remarked, blending a touch of contempt with her indifference.

'And there is another reason,' Margaret said, with reluctance.

'Of course there is another reason. You are afraid my attractions might prove too strong for his sensitive nature. Naturally I divined that.'

Margaret laughed.

'Well, you know, it wouldn't be at all odd if he did fall in love with you, but I should be sorry, because it would only make him unhappy,' she rejoined, with some spirit. Gallia smiled out over the park. 'You may laugh,' continued Margaret. 'I know you don't believe in men having feelings like ours.'

'On the contrary, not like ours, but simply the counterpart of ours.'

'Hubert is a curious, silent creature, but that is not to say that he has no heart.'

'Very true.'

'Gallia, you are laughing again! What has made you so hard upon men generally?'

'Me hard upon men? What a wild idea! I like men extremely. I'm more at ease with them than I am with women; I've known far more of them intimately. I'm not sure that I don't think their make-up much honester than women's. How can you call me hard upon them?' She argued with the greatest good-humour, for she was attached to Margaret, and liked Margaret to assault her. 'Simply because I have dared to burst their cocoons; to wind off some of the strange silky poetry that has been wrapped round them by generations of women and their fellow-men. I don't believe all this about men's feelings, because I've never come across any of it; that's why. I explain such evidences in a totally different way, and I claim that my way is a great deal more in accordance with the facts. There you have it.'

'The long and the short of it is, that you don't believe in love,' said Margaret simply, and with a small air of offence. 'But you will fall in love yourself some day, and then you will see what it is like.'

Gallia's cheek darkened for a second, then her face cleared, and she leaned far back in the window-seat they were occupying, and passed her hand up and down the shining cold edge of the old-fashioned rose-patterned chintz curtain.

There fell a long silence between them. Gallia felt no inclination to make any reply: she did not even realise that the moment was one eminently suited to confidences; and if she had, it would have made no difference. She had never experienced, in all her life, the faintest desire to confide in anybody. This reserved habit of mind made her, at one and the same time, in some things so wise, and in many things so ignorant. Margaret saw her flush, and felt a moment's expectation; then she divined that, though Gallia might be, or have been, in love, she had no desire to describe her experiences. She broke silence, therefore, in a half-whispering voice.

'I have heard it said,' she began curiously, 'that every man is a widower when he proposes.'

'Ah! Have you indeed?' Gallia was roused from her abstraction and gleamed with dark humour upon the speaker.

'And yet,' Margaret continued, in a hesitating manner and with a little lurking hope in her voice – 'And yet one always hopes, if one *did* fall in love some day, it would be with a man who had been as little of a widower as possible!'

The humour of this speech threatened to overcome Gallia's gravity; in spite of Margaret's touching earnestness, she would have given way to a strong desire to laugh, perhaps, unless she had had a very clear motive in hearing the girl's views frankly and confidently expressed.

'Instinctively, then, you dislike the idea?'

'Oh, I think it dreadful! Everyone must.'

'Do you think it dreadful all the time – or only when it is brought home to you in connection with one of your acquaintances?'

'Well, of course it's a thing one tries to think of as little as possible,' Margaret said emphatically.

Gallia noted this with a certain bird-like alertness of glance.

'But every time it *does* come into my head it horrifies me; of course, more than ever about a man I know.'

For the moment Gallia could not be quite sure whether this referred to an experience, or whether Magaret spoke prospectively. She waited. The speaker continued musingly –

'As a rule, I suppose it is just about men whom you know that you don't hear of it.'

A caustic smile hovered on Miss Hamesthwaite's lips.

'I believe it is a canon of decency to conceal such facts; one owes it to one's women friends, men think. But, Margaret, if you knew and liked a man – if he was a friend, you know – you wouldn't dislike him if you discovered that he had a mistress, for instance?'

Margaret turned a much-startled face from the window.

'How' – she began, and then suddenly recovered her composure. 'I shouldn't dislike him – as a friend – I suppose.'

'But – as a lover?'

'Oh,' she cried quickly, 'I could not bear him as a lover!'

'But, my dear girl, men being what they are, is that reasonable?'

'Oh, there is a difference between believing a thing to be generally the case, and knowing it to be the fact. Oh, *do* say there is.'

'Oh, surely. And there's a difference to an ostrich who has his head buried – or hasn't, as time and opportunity have allowed.'

'Gallia, you are fearfully severe. I suppose there are some girls – the Gertrude sort of girls, you know – who don't mind at all. But most girls – of some heart and feeling – most girls do feel it dreadfully.'

'If a man were here, he would exclaim piously, "And God grant there may always be such girls in the world, or what hope has a man of keeping straight!"' Gallia laughed delightedly. 'Yes, we have proved there are three sorts of women. The bad ones, to fan the flame of men's vices – a red flame that, for the sake of the picturesque; the good girls, to feed the white flame of their virtues; and the in-between girl, who blows neither fire, and can warm herself indifferently at both.'

'But you, Gallia, you? You have never said what you think of it.'

'Oh, for me, I would love any man who attracted my mind, who shared my tastes – I mean my sort of love, you know; but it would be independent of any idea of marriage. To a certain extent, then, and with regard to marrying, I think my ideas on other points lead to my preferring the ordinary man.' This she said very thoughtfully, and with a marked, earnest voice. 'There are a lot of passionless men about nowadays,' she went on in an easier tone, 'and it would be terrible to marry one by mistake. Yes, I have decided. It is quite reasonable – which is the main thing. I shall make no fuss about it if my future husband has a past – of a reasonable colour.'

'I think – if I loved a man' – Margaret's face and voice partook of an ideally exquisite quality as she spoke – 'I think I could forgive him.'

Gallia gazed at her in admiration.

'You are the being biology will never explain. You keep alive the old tradition about soul, and angels, and saints, and spirits. No scientist living but would forswear his whole life's labour for you if he saw you at this moment! Wouldn't he, now?'

'Nonsense, Gallia! I am nothing of the kind.' She laughed charmingly. 'Though, of course, I know' – with a great attempt at frankness – 'that I am pretty.'

'You beautiful, silly soul! I believe you honestly think that's all that's the matter with you. Come down, and let us get the letters which have just trotted across the park on Punch's back.'

They ran downstairs together, and fell upon the post-bag in the hall.

'Ah, more excitement! The great man from Africa arrives in London tomorrow, and – goodness! – this is from Robbie Leighton. He's in Paris. He's coming – when? Oh, I'm to expect him when I see him.'

Margaret made some comment or other, but her pensiveness lasted all the afternoon. Perhaps she was going to be called upon to forgive him – a part women have ever loved to play.

Chapter Twenty-Five

Quite the typical country-house party was gathered beside the cedars one afternoon some few days later. It was the kind of day upon which no object was quite still before the eye, every tree and flower seemed to tremble, rather to shiver lightly, in the gold heat, which was so intense as to appear solid, corporeal, to lie like a weight upon the earth.

While tea went on under the trees, the light oak luggage-cart could be seen upon the winding drive making its way downhill towards the high road and the station. Just in front had passed a pretty pair-horse victoria, and it was quite in keeping with stable etiquette that the victoria drawn by the two fretting thoroughbreds should start slowly in advance, and the luggage-cart, which flew easily, behind a less important equine character, should come after.

John Denyer was expected from London, where he had passed a few days on his arrival, and whither Lord Hamesthwaite had travelled three times to see him on important business.

From one of these visits the Colonial Secretary had returned with a question to put to his daughter. It had taken her a good deal by surprise.

'Ask Mr Gurdon down here? Oh, surely, if you like. But why am I to write? You know him, papa, I suppose better than I do?'

'I have seen him perhaps three times socially. I met him at your Aunt Celia's one night a little time ago; and I have happened to meet him twice or three times since –'

'And you met him at a dinner at the Reform last year, for I recollect you told me of it,' Gallia put in.

'Very true, no doubt; but it had escaped me.'

'And in your own department too!'

'In my own department I have of course been *aware* of him, my dear, but I have not known him.'

'I suppose he is a mere menial in the department?' said Gallia wickedly, for she was not above laughing occasionally at her father's pomposity. For a wonder Lord Hamesthwaite decided to take this seriously.

'I greatly wish, Gallia, that you had acquired some of your dear mother's genius for comprehending important social matters! Mr Gurdon is a very remarkable young man. His sagacity,' Lord Hamesthwaite continued, as though he were referring to a water-spaniel – 'his sagacity is amazing. Quite amazing. I am not mistaken when I tell you that Gurdon is a man with a career before him. He is not yet thirty, and he has been singled out. Besides, he is most gentlemanly and of charming manners. Denyer took a great liking to him when they met in Africa.'

'Oh! So he met Denyer in Africa? I never heard him say so.'

'You have indicated his greatest talent. He is a young man who does not feel it necessary to say everything that he knows or that he has done.'

Gallia might not have a head for affairs, but she was quite sharp enough to know that this was very high praise. She had often heard her Aunt Celia say that Mark should be helped on, and she was able to perceive that he was in a fair way to have her father's hand reached down to him.

'Shall we therefore say Thursday?' Lord Hamesthwaite inquired, with a smile. He was a great deal too courteous to leave his daughter with the recollection of something like a reprimand from him in her mind.

'Yes, I'll ask him for Thursday, papa.'

Lord Hamesthwaite turned rather nervously towards her on his way to the door.

'You don't dislike Mr Gurdon, Gallia, I hope?'

'*Tout au contraire*,'* she replied lightly, 'I like him very much.'

The discussion ended, the note was written, Gurdon was free, and would be delighted, and consequently arrived in correct form in time for luncheon on Thursday. The same afternoon, a dishevelled young man stepped out of a station fly, with a battered brown bag in his hand, and bade the footman be careful of the foreign-looking packages he was taking from the hands of the driver.

'Good gracious!' exclaimed Gallia, who was at that moment issuing from the hall door, accompanied by Margaret. 'It is Robbie.' Margaret could have told her as much, for it was indeed no other.

The young man swept a Spanish sombrero from his head with an insouciance that was native and a flourish that was foreign, and disclosed the astonishing effect produced by a person having hair much fairer than his skin.

He shook Gallia heartily by the hand, keeping his eyes well upon her face and his sombrero at his side.

'Miss Essex I once had the pleasure of knowing in Paris,' he said, with a neat little emphasis, just marked enough for Margaret to hear, upon the 'once'.

'I have not forgotten you at all,' said the exquisite Margaret, with a tender music in her voice, and upon her face a smile only just large enough to love.

'Good Heavens! passionately attached to each other, I declare,' said Gallia inwardly, and reflected further that a charming scamp like Mr Robert Leighton was precisely the kind of being Margaret was framed to waste herself upon.

Robbie's behaviour from the first hour of his arrival left no doubt of his feeling to Margaret, and Gurdon, for one, observed it with much peace of mind.

He was extravagantly charming to Mrs Essex – utterly enthralled by Margaret, of whom he made sketches in a dozen fictitious characters, and of whom he immediately undertook a serious portrait.

This very portrait was under discussion as they sat at tea, awaiting, on Gallia's part with some excitement, the arrival of John Denyer.

'Now look here,' Robbie exclaimed, leaping up wildly with a teacup in his hand. 'My idea is to have her here – Miss Essex, do you mind – just half a minute? Thanks – by this pink peony

tree. In this same pink gown. No hat on. Drenched in sunlight –
you see?'

'She will have sunstroke to a certainty,' cried her mother.

'Face, hair, hands, all that wonderful gold shade,' Robbie
went on, with unabated enthusiasm – 'that grey atmospheric
gold; and then the peonies and the dress – masses of bluish-
purple.'

'But they are pink,' suggested someone diffidently.

'Actually, but not relatively!' cried Robbie with much fervour.
'Actually we *know* they are pink. Relatively we *see* they are
bluish-purple. One paints what one sees.'

An impressive silence followed this explanation of the method
of art.

'Then I am of course going to do a head in the old Italian
manner, with a gold background. Gold is Miss Essex's inevitable
setting. But it is among flowers that a large portrait should seize
her. Dear Miss Essex – is it troubling you too much? Just over
here. The pink of your gown is simply inspired! I see a most
fascinating scheme, by using that sheet of poker-red nasturtiums
as a background.'

They strolled off together, amid a chorus of laughter and
shrieks of horror; but the earnest-minded artist and his victim
heeded them not, and it may be stated in Robbie's defence that
he did paint that picture, and that it acted as an extinguisher to
some two hundred and fifty other pictures in the centre of a
room at the Grafton Galleries.

Gurdon was a silent member of the party. He had wondered
why no one wanted to paint Gallia, a slim, silvery figure with a
dense blue-green feathered arm of the cedar behind her.

Her old plainness of attire was no longer indulged in. Whether
she thought it seemly, as the hostess of a large establishment, or
whether it was the outcome of but another personal whim,
Gallia had chosen to be rather magnificent in her costume of
late.

From her head, on which she wore one of those French rustic
hats, with cobwebs of lace draped over the brim, so unbecoming
to almost every Englishwoman, to her feet and ankles in their

silvery-grey stockings and grey leather buckled shoes, she was perfect. Sitting with her legs crossed, the dove-coloured ruffle of her petticoat – pale ashes of roses tint – was a delight to see, and perhaps it was because he enjoyed looking at her so much, that Mark found little to say.

Mrs Essex was not a talkative woman, but she was a good listener, and little Lord Shillinglee, a young man of enormous wealth and no fixed political opinions, was giving her plenty to listen to.

'Ah, you see they haven't got the money, Mrs Essex; these Radical fellows 'll promise anything to a man who will back them up a bit with some money. I'm a bit of a Radical myself, you know, though this lawn isn't the place to say so, eh? And I really shouldn't mind going in with them, if it was only to hear the other side curse – I beg your pardon, Mrs Essex, but they would, you know.' He dissolved in a malicious little chuckle, and shook furtively within his baggy clothing.

Gallia looked down at him, where he sprawled awkwardly at one side of her, and then over to Mark sprawling gracefully at the other. Her mind was busy with the contrast when the carriage came up to the front door. Lord Hamesthwaite at once went to receive the short, well-built man who got down from it.

'Ah, there is Mr Denyer,' said Mrs Essex, and the eyes of the party were for the moment directed to the group. A few minutes later the great man was among them. Mark Gurdon's eye never left Miss Hamesthwaite when the introduction was being performed. All her whims of manner, the scorns and ironies and indifferences of youth, dropped from her, and left a picture of the woman she would be in a few years' time, when her slow development had progressed.

Only the ease and dignity natural to her position, as well as the graciousness that was her own, appeared in the pleasant words of welcome that she spoke. A certain glow rose in Gurdon's mind, as he caught this glimpse of the stately and social Gallia he had seen once before, with a difference, at Holland House. Entirely without 'beauty manners' at all times, Gallia sometimes lacked something of the influence the manners of a beautiful young woman give her. It is most fortunate that the generality of beautiful people behave as though they were beautiful – for this, not their actual claims of form and feature, is what the mass of mankind observes and responds to.

Denyer had been moving among the groups, but he came and stood beside Gallia and looked across the park. The figure of Mr Essex, in his light-grey clothes, was seen crossing the grass to the house.

'Ah, Miss Hamesthwaite, can you guess what it is to a man whose eyes have been accustomed to the far lovelier flowers of our Dark Continent, to see again a sward, moist and velvety, freckled with daisies?'

Gallia responded intently to the touch of real emotion in the man's voice. She was interested. Her greeting to Essex was unconsciously shortened.

'How exquisite your Surrey is! A garden, a series of parterres. One of oak forest, one of chestnut plantation, one of meadow grass, one corn or flowers.'

'It must seem wonderfully small to you. But it is rich, really very rich – and would go so much further if the people knew anything about exploiting it. You, in Africa, can compel settlers to the use of more scientific means of cultivation; nothing compels them here!' Gallia spoke with a note of regret and bitterness, then stopped to give Mr Denyer a cup of the tea that had just been brought out.

'Expensive business trying to start new agricultural methods in this country!' remarked Lord Shillinglee, who had abandoned agriculture for coal, and saw no reason to regret it.

'Very, eh, Gallia?' cried Robbie, with the air of acute mischief. 'Let me see, what did your van* cost when you were so hot on agricultural reform?'

'Miss Hamesthwaite, this is news!' cried Mark, much interested. 'How much truth is there in the accusation of philanthropy?'

Gallia turned to him, smiling. 'I'm afraid a good deal,' she replied. 'Others enjoy telling that story more than I do – ask papa about it.'

Lord Hamesthwaite appeared nothing loth to provide details.

'Ah, those were the days of our enthusiasm,' he said, in a good-natured, quizzing fashion. 'We attended the classes at an agricultural college throughout a whole session. Then we started a van, and selected our own teachers.'

'Then it was partly your scheme?' enquired Mrs Essex.

'Not at all! I was severely neutral. This young woman did the whole thing. Let me see – *what* did the van teach, Gallia?'

'Farmyard Economics,' said Gallia briefly, suppressing a smile.

A low, delighted chuckle from Essex greeted the reply.

'It wasn't agriculture, it was simply, as I say, Farmyard Economics we wanted to teach. We weren't in connection with, far less in opposition to, any of the efforts made by the societies; but I thought, and for that matter still think, there was room for the practical enlightened common sense our people talked. My two young men lectured in turns in the van.'

'Of course free?' from Gurdon.

'Oh, certainly, free!'

'The expense was all upon the other side,' said Robbie, laughing. 'It cost a pretty penny to compel them to come in to the van, didn't it, Gallia?'

'You will never be happy till I tell you what it did cost,' Gallia said, looking over to him.

'For how long did you pursue the idea?' Denyer enquired.

'For a season, commencing in the middle of February and continuing to the beginning of June.'

'Well, it cost just a fraction over a thousand pounds,' said Gallia reluctantly. This statement excited much delighted laughter.

'Farmyard Economics!' murmured Essex in a tone of irresistible gravity.

Gallia swept round upon him.

'Well, I paid two young men, bought two horses from papa – and he let me have them very cheap, I remember they were £40 apiece. Then I had to have the van built. It was a beautiful van, painted in grass-green and corn-colour, with appropriate mottoes – no, I will *not* divulge the mottoes round the top. That van cost over £200, although I designed every bit of it myself – '

There was more laughter, in which Gallia joined frankly.

'But what industry and application on your part, Miss Hamesthwaite!' Denyer said, looking admiringly upon the beautiful face.

Gallia coloured.

'I was just growing up,' she said, more seriously, and with a return to the irony of her ordinary mood. 'I had been too well fed, I suppose, all my life, and I had a good deal of superfluous energy to work off. Besides, I was just at the age of devotion and anxiety to do good, and that sort of thing. It didn't last long, and of course I see the folly of it now.'

This speech affected various of her hearers very differently.

Gurdon's face, in spite of his enjoyment of the details of her scheme, had been alight with interest and admiration. He had thought that Gallia *affairée** would be a more charming picture – a reality – than any other Gallia. He thought that eagerness and warmth and interest must have greatly become her dark beauty, which a touch of too much cynicism made somewhat inhuman.

Denyer, experienced man and diplomat, leader, organiser, financier, and ruler, was interested too, because he was faced by something he did not understand, and could not account for. To Denyer nothing that he did not understand was small or unimportant. The mere fact that he did not understand it gave it a certain importance in his eyes.

Essex, with eyes half-shut and blinking at long intervals beneath his hat brim, scrutinised less her face than her mental attitude. The mere details of her expression were less noticed by him than a scarcely perceptible uneven shifting of her figure.

'In Miss Hamesthwaite's mind philanthropy appears to rank as an intellectual nettle-rash,' he observed critically. 'Some people get nettle-rash at forty.'

Gallia had fallen into a smiling melancholy.

'It's usually a youthful disease, all the same,' she said. 'I have been so long growing up,' she continued, with an air as though she had just perceived the fact. 'You know when you are grown up because you accept things. I scarcely can yet, I want to fight everything and have everything new and made new again.'

Denyer and Gurdon smiled discreetly and politely in admiration of her lighted face.

'What an innocent lady!' said Essex sweetly. 'Still at the age of comparatives. Good. Bad. Indifferent.'

She turned to him.

'Prophesy, if you like,' she cried. 'I know you want to! That I shall come to an even mean, yes? Well, it is quite possible.'

Chapter Twenty-Six

There are only two kinds of people in society, and each kind is admittedly equally tedious. There is the person who thinks one should 'be oneself' at all hazards, and the person who thinks that at no hazard should one be oneself, but always someone else.

At the first blush, the first-named commends himself most to an honest mind, but before declaring for him it may be well to pause.

Change and recreation are the inevitable food of man. Sooner or later the human being who has decided in favour of 'being oneself' will take a holiday, draw a long breath, and decide, for refreshment's sake, to be someone else. It is at this juncture that you may meet him, and how are you to know?

Equally inconvenient, and even more common, is the second breed of human – he whose creed perceives a certain indecency, at any rate an impoliteness and an inexpediency, in being oneself, and who is customarily engaged in being someone else. This person is equally certain to pack his bag, so to say; expand his chest, and, with defiance in his eye and custom beneath his heel, decide to 'be himself'. And if at this point you have fallen in with him – well, how *are* you to know?

The worst of the business is, that it is usually on the occasion of a handsome crisis in their lives that people behave in this way. And if you yourself are mixed up in the crisis – if it is your crisis too? At any rate, there is comfort in knowing that a crisis is the finest setting for a mistake. Seldom, if ever, does a mistake have fair play and become fully recognised unless it is made at a crisis.

Fortunately, it usually is, and that is why we hear so much about mistakes.

When Dark Essex kissed and passionately loved Gallia in the Cloisters of Westminster – was he being himself or someone else? And was it his moment of change, or his age of custom? Had he prefaced his *abandon* with this unspoken flash of thought: 'By Heavens, I'll act like any other man'? Or with this: 'For once, then, a mad once, I'll let myself go'? Gallia had often wondered. So had Essex. It formed an interesting speculation for his leisure moments, and to facilitate its study he sought Gallia's society – or rather her neighbourhood – from time to time. As a part of this seeking, he decided to accept the invitation for the day on Hindhead.

The advent of Miss Janion to the Hall had decided Gallia on making this expedition; she entertained a wholesome fear of the 'maiden-up-to-date', if left, for whole consecutive hours, loose about the house and grounds. Gertrude was a person who liked to 'do something'. She came down in the best of clothes, and consequently in the best of spirits too, prepared to do any number of things, and in appropriate dresses.

'Shillinglee?' she cried, as Gallia ran over the names of the house party. 'How amusing! How *is* it, I wonder, that one never goes to a country house without meeting the man one last refused? And he always takes you down to dinner, too.'

'Well, in point of fact, I had –' Gallia began vaguely.

'I know! Of course; you had arranged it! My dear, don't alter the table for me. I've gone through it with others, and I can again.'

Gallia laughed. 'You'll accept him this time,' she said.

'Shall I? I believe I shall. He said so the other day at the Prince's garden party, I remember. What a gathering! Never in all my life have I seen –' and so the chitter-chatter had run on.

While the household was still at breakfast, there was heard the heavy clopping of under-bred hoofs upon the drive, and when they looked out, there was Essex, mounted on some strange quadruped he had hired from his inn at Hiddenfold.

'Ah, but you haven't felt him trot!' he said, with academic gravity, as he came into the breakfast hall and shook hands.

'You see he is accustomed to working front horse in a team of three. I call him, most incorrectly, the Teamster.'

'Well, I think you had better abandon him and see what we can do,' Lord Hamesthwaite called from his little table near the fire.

Breakfast was agreeably broken up at three little tables, and Gallia and Margaret were in a square window embrasure, supported by Gurdon and Lord Shillinglee.

Robbie was described as not up yet. Mrs Essex was described as not down yet. Gertrude was described as not dressed yet.

Everyone admitted that it was a lovely day. Mr Essex sank into a chair and tapped his boots.

Gallia noted, with a feeling of dislike, when she handed him a peach with a bit of ice in place of the stone, that his feet were too small. In the Cloisters, just when he took her hands, she had observed that his hands were too small. It was a blemish in so handsome a man; a blemish that gave her a feeling of discomfort.

They were to start in twenty minutes.

'Now may I order you something that corresponds to one's idea of a horse – or will you prefer driving?' she said hospitably.

For a second the crazed suggestion lightened in Essex's brain that he would first like to know if *she* were riding or driving. Then he reflected, sensibly, that of course he wouldn't have cared to know anything of the kind.

Any woman would have perceived that Gallia's snowy spotted muslin was never put on to be taken off again in such a hurry.

In her hat she had followed Margaret's plan; it arched eave-like above her hair; but over it, as she was driving, she had carried a broad wisp of incredibly soft French *lisse*,* which broke in a foaming bow under her chin.

Beside her, Margaret, in the green of young willows, and a hat trimmed with their garlands, seemed the most delectable of summer morsels. Gertrude wore a coaching dress from Paris, which had to be seen to be credited. In time they started. Gallia drove Mr Denyer behind her Norfolk trotter. The main party came on the coach, Lord Shillinglee proudly exercising his only known and proven talent, handling with beautiful dexterity what Gallia called her scratch team.

The picturesquely English start from the fine old house was greatly enhanced by the solitary equestrian. Mr Essex had abandoned the Teamster to the heaviest oats the brute had ever encountered, and was mounted on Gallia's black hunter. This exquisite beast had not done a day's work for many months, and only enough exercise to keep him in condition. When he came out of the stable, shining like a looking-glass, and as supple as a Persian cat, Gallia apologised for his flesh.

'If you are determined to ride, you shall at least have a good day,' she said, as she looked over his bitting with a careful eye. 'Spain's paces are really divine.'

Spain proceeded to illustrate this the moment his rider's weight was in the saddle.

'You could ride him on a thread of silk,' Gallia said proudly, as she watched the beast playing with his feet, 'but you'll soon see what Spain is made of.'

'Liquorice and *aguardiénte*,* I should think,' said Robbie.

Gurdon looked on, and wished he had been riding also. No man should miss an opportunity of riding when he wants to make an impression on a woman, provided he never loses his temper with a horse, and *can* ride.

'When you first went to Spain, how did you make yourself understood in the wild places?' an obvious association of ideas led Margaret to ask, as they bowled down the avenue.

'Oh, I learnt some Spanish in Paris; short sentences, you know. There was a little girl there, daughter of an old model, who put lots of useful tips in my way. Of course you remember young Lemuel, Gurdon?' He leaned over and threw this question behind Lord Hamesthwaite's shoulders to Mark.

'Oh yes, perfectly,' Gurdon answered, wondering what had put the girl into Robbie's mind. But he was destined to receive no information, for Robbie was a scatter-brain, and any notions of sequence in conversation were foreign to his type.

Gurdon had excellent reason not to forget the girl; at that moment he had in his pocket a brief note from her, forwarded from his club. She was still in Brighton; she was almost strong. 'It was so gay and jolly after town; she hoped he was amusing himself wherever he was. She had got the cheque all right. The doctor thought another fortnight would quite set her up; he was such a nice doctor; quite young; he had sent her tickets for two afternoon concerts.' He mentally conned over all the short, shallow sentences. He was sorry for the girl, not because of her position, but because of her nature. She must so certainly go one way. A man's most pleasing inconsistency is his earnest pity of an unfortunate. It gives the good people hope of his redemption; it assures the average, clear-headed people that there is no possible hope of hers.

He was sitting where he could see a stretch of exquisite country on every side of him; feeling the exhilaration in the light rush of summer air; within touch of the fluttering laces that came warm from Margaret's neck and tapped his cheek, and were recovered and apologised for, made fast and blown loose again – Margaret, the woman he had at one time thought he loved. In front of him, a bright speck upon the road, sometimes basely swallowed by a covetous hedge curve or a greedy group of trees, was the little cart crowned by the white figure of Gallia. Sitting there, it struck him that surely no man ever saw the cobweb threads of his destiny so thickly floating in the air before him. Now one tickled his face and now another. Now it was Margaret and her whilom charm that he thought of; now it was Gallia and the strong fascination she had for him. Then it was the letter in his pocket. He remembered that other coach drive in Paris two years ago, when he had sat beside Mont Voisin and talked horse-breeding in the latest *cuvée** of Paris French – when he had been troubled by those underthoughts about his career. Then he had not been getting on. Since? Well, since had come his private secretaryship – not to the man he wanted, but still, to a very good man. Then Denyer's return home, unexpected, too good to hope for, as it had seemed. And a few chance words must have passed between Denyer and Lord Hamesthwaite. The Colonial Secretary must now know what he had owed, frankly and directly, to the discretion of one humble underling in the big office; an underling who, happening to have a little money, had conceived the idea of spending his two months' rest in Africa, the country whose name was under his eyes some fifty times a day. Lord Hamesthwaite must know, or wherefore this sudden patronage? Mark was far too clever to think of it as anything else. Life seen from *this* coach-top was somewhat different, indeed! His alertness had served him very well. So had money which he had put away carefully when his father died, and there was more of it left yet.

A less acute young Englishman would never have imagined it worth his while to take the particular journey Mark had taken; to fall into intercourse with the particular men Mark had thought it well to meet; to get to know the facts of a case as Mark had got to know them; to earn the personal commendation of the strong man on the spot, John Denyer; to ignore the fact of his connection with the big office at home as Mark had ignored it; to come home and hold his tongue about the whole business as Mark had held his.

'*Distrait*, am I? I beg your pardon!' he said, in answer to a playful poke from Mrs Essex. 'I was thinking about the last time I was coaching; it was from Paris to Auteuil and back. I was thinking of the astonishing difference in the outlook.'

'Ah, quite so. The races, I suppose? Oh, a very gay scene in France, of course. I remember, when I paid my daughter a visit, we were driving, and saw the people coming back from Longchamps. Different indeed! One could not imagine a sweet Surrey road holding such a company.'

They were pulling up the steep winding ascent to Hindhead, the breath of the pines was about them, the air was full of the hum of ardent bees constraining the heather to an early bloom. Upon the links of road visible some mile or two behind was Essex on the slim black Spain. In front was the green cart, with the brilliant Norfolk bay throwing himself at his collar, and Gallia's smiling face turned backward, as it seemed, looking at him. Gurdon's road had changed indeed.

Chapter Twenty-Seven

'You see, it's not as though I had a sixpence in the world.' Mr Leighton raised himself to a more upright position on the heather, and made the familiar gesture of pulling his watch from his pocket. 'Look here!' the chain came out neatly, and was found to have a curious piece of copper money attached to it. 'You see what time it is with me!' he added, with a touch of easy tragedy.

'Oh, you don't really mean –'

He interrupted the soft note of shocked amusement in Margaret's voice.

'Indeed I do. Had to, positively, to get down here.'

'How dreadful for you!'

'So we should be as poor as possible at first. But not for long. I have lots of old stuff that would feed the Spring Exhibitions for some time to come. And I should paint portraits. I should get on at that, I know. You see, to be a portrait-painter, you only want two things.' Robbie screwed up his face and tried to look practical. 'You want to paint the right people, and you want to paint 'em in the right way.'

'Yes,' said Margaret, with deep sympathy in her face.

'Now, as to the right people, I should be in rare case. Grannie would help me to rope in the right people.' She nodded. 'And as to the right way – well, you *see* my way in that big *plein air* I'm doing of you.'

'You mean the grey, gold, and bluish-purple one?' She might well ask. Robbie had at least five canvases on the way.

'Yes, that's it. I'm painting people in greyish gold and purple just now. I mean, that's how I see them, you know. Well, after all, a man only wants a manner.' He put his hand through his yellow hair and pulled several stray locks down over his cedar-coloured forehead. 'So that we should be perfectly independent, you know; I'm sure you couldn't bear to feel dependent on anyone, and I know I couldn't. And Grannie makes a lovely background to a fellow's life.'

Margaret laughed. She was one of those women with a silver laugh. They are really the nicest kind.

'Oh, Robbie,' she cried, 'don't make yourself out such a dreadful goose and such a naughty boy as well, or I don't think I really can –'

'Now don't say it, Margaret, or you'll regret it! You do love me, you must love me, for I have loved you ever since that day in Paris when I first saw you. You remember ? It was your first morning at the studio, and you didn't know your way about. I shall never forget the colour in your face when it dawned on you that you were in the wrong studio. You looked divine! The fellows talked of you all morning.'

'It was one of the most frightful moments of my life,' said Margaret faintly.

'By Heavens, what a subject picture that would be! I see the whole thing; I should treat it as an upright. Your face would be the warmest note of colour, the prevailing tones would be grey, and the faint pinks of the model would support your pink blush. I shall do it! I shall call it "A Rose in Error". No, "An Errant Rose". You wait.'

'Robbie, you think of nothing but painting me.'

'You're wrong. I think much more of loving you. I have thought of that since ever I've known you.'

'Hush!' She raised up a white and very pointed forefinger. 'Don't say that. There was one time when you didn't think of me at all. But we won't talk of it any more.' She sighed and drooped her serious eyes.

'My darling girl, we must talk of it, if you are to be so madly mistaken as all that. I swear that I have loved you ever since I have seen you. I may have been a bit wild. I may not have been all the time just what you would have wished me to be – and what your love will always keep me.' He took her hand and kissed it, and looked up at her with deep sincerity in his face.

She responded to it by leaning forward and putting her lips to his forehead. It was the first time she had volunteered the smallest caress, and for a moment he lost his head. It was much credit to him that he found it again, and continued. 'But you have kept me straight.' This he said, spacing the words to give them more emphasis. She looked at him rather wonderingly. 'Why, dear, you can't imagine the things I might have been up to in Paris.'

'*Don't* tell me, Robbie! I'd much rather not know.'

'My dear child, I wasn't going to tell you. How can you suppose that I would?' He put both his arms round her, which brought his head on her shoulder, since she was seated on a tree-root somewhat above him. 'Don't let us talk of it any more now, dear. There is nothing, Margaret, I swear it to you, nothing that any good woman would not be able to forgive. You know there are vast differences in men; I can't explain 'em to you exactly, but there are. I don't lay claim to many shining virtues, but among men, you know, and *by* men, you understand, I should come out pretty well. For I've never been a bad chap, really.'

Whether memory suppressed an echo in Margaret's mind cannot be told; at any rate, they were very happy after this, so happy that they forgot everybody but themselves; which is the only trustworthy symptom of true happiness. Fortunately, most of the party had expected that this picnic would 'bring matters to a head' between Mr Leighton and Miss Essex. The dependence of the upper classes in England upon picnics as an emotional opportunity is positively pathetic. The excellent meal, which forms the inevitable prelude to that moment at which one may get away and talk with the only person one desires to talk to, was over. It had been accompanied by no greater excitement than a wonder as to what had become of Mr Essex. He had been at most a mile a half behind them when last seen, and yet he had never appeared.

A footman had been despatched to the inn at which he had been advised to leave Spain, and had returned with the curious intelligence that the horse was in the stable and that Mr Essex was in the inn. Mr Essex had asked for a room, and some ink, pens, and paper, and had left orders that he was not to be disturbed.

'Seized with an inopportune attack of literary creativeness,' Gurdon had observed, smiling; and nobody found a better explanation to offer.

'Such an odd boy he always was!' his mother plaintively added, not without some pride in his oddity, however.

So lunch had passed over without him, and then Margaret and Robbie had wandered off, taking advantage of irregularities in the rolling heathland and other bits of cover with a deftness that would have put a detachment of infantry to the blush.

The rest permitted an opposite direction to attract them, and strolled quietly along, Denyer and Mark Gurdon walking on each side of Gallia at first. There was nothing particular to do. The object of the expedition had been the drive, and they were to drive home by another road, which would give them an extra five miles and a great deal of delightful scenery.

Returning from the walk, Gallia went on in advance to give her orders about putting in the horses. Leaning up against the coach she discovered Mr Essex, with that peculiar air of coolness, paleness, and dark handsomeness that distinguished him.

'Really, at the top of that three-mile hill, Spain and I had worked so hard that we were both unfit to join the party. The landlord deeply sympathised with my condition, and he and his man put me through a wonderful twenty minutes. It seems they have a great experience in towelling the cyclists. After that I lay down; after that, I am ashamed to say, I went to sleep.' These explanations flowed smoothly from Mr Essex, and wore an air of such truth that the footman packing a hamper close by paused in his work and marvelled.

Gallia had turned to Mrs Essex with some laughing allusion to the cause of her son's disappearance.

'Do not be any quicker than you can help with the horses,' Essex remarked, catching the groom's eye and bidding adieu to half a sovereign at the same moment. The man understood him, and passed the word to his helpers.

'May I claim the last ten minutes of this delightful hour, Miss Hamesthwaite?' Essex said, approaching her as she stood in brisk talk with Mark Gurdon. She looked up at him at once – the curious still atmosphere of strength and hidden thought about the man always commanded her attention. 'I should like to show you the greatest curiosity in the neighbourhood, and I think you may have missed it. It lies over here.'

'Mr Essex excites my interest!' she said to Mark. 'Well, then, don't disappear when Brownie is put in, because she will not stand, and you know I am to drive you home.'

Whether this remark disturbed Essex or not, he certainly spoke no word as they walked off together.

'But you said it was over there?' protested Gallia, pointing with her parasol, and then opening it suddenly.

'Truly,' he rejoined, altering the direction of his steps. Still they went on in silence.

'What were you doing at the inn?' Gallia asked, as they descended a hill among the pine trees.

'I was writing to you,' answered Essex quietly.

'To me?' – she looked up in surprise at his face.

With a sudden change of his absorbed manner, he met her eyes and put life into his glance.

'To you. See this!' he showed her an envelope with her name upon it. 'Shall we sit down here on the edge of this little pool? It looks deep, doesn't it?'

Gallia was conscious that the day had changed, that her frame of mind must alter to be in keeping with it, that something serious was coming to her. There was no fascination, no magnetism about Essex's glance, but there was, now and then, a curious deep, still fondness in its depths, which lingered for a very little moment, just long enough to obtain recognition, and then left mockery, of himself as much as others, in its place.

'I have changed my mind about my letter: I shall throw it away,' he said.

'Don't do that! It would spoil the heather.'

Essex laughed.

'What a pity I am not a sentimental fellow!' said he; 'there is a beautiful opportunity for bitterness there. No, we will dig a hole – and bury it. Some little mice will gnaw it up and make nests of it, and still smaller mice, of a fleshy shade, shall nestle in it – good.' He began to make a hole just between them as they sat. Still digging, efficiently enough, with a long silver cross that hung on his watch-chain but never dangled publicly upon his waistcoat, he began speaking.

'Don't be impatient, Gallia: this is the last of me.'

'What is?'

'This little talk today, and this buried letter.'

'Don't bury the letter – let me read it first.'

'And bury it after? No, indeed. Some letters are meant to be buried. I see that in any case you would wish this one buried, so my last service shall be to bury it for you.'

'Your last – and your first service.'

He looked up.

'That's not true. I have done, first and last, a great deal for you, Gallia. First and last, good or bad, I have done a great deal. For six years I have been a great deal in your life; often I have involuntarily given the tendency to your thoughts. When we met, what were you like? Ah! how different you were!'

'I remember myself perfectly. I could cry now for what I suffered! How hard I have taken everything! How brackish and bitter every experience of my first youth tasted! Drowned in sea-water, life has been for me. I was hot-spirited, raw, impatient; clever, sensitive, shy, vain, self-conscious; with an abnormally developed sense of the ridiculous; too shy even to cherish a fine ideal inside myself. Then you came along, and how much bitterer and more brackish things seemed to you! What a cynicism I found in you! What crude brutality you served out to me!' She recapitulated these things as though they had been long unthought of in her mind, as though she saw and recognised them clearly now at last for the first time. Neither looked at the other, they stared out across the wonderful waves of green Surrey far into the blue of Sussex.

'Yes, I spoilt you and warped you – unintentionally, of course. I used to think of you much more than I would ever admit, you know. Then, when I was tutoring in Greece and trailing cubs* about Asia – those strange letters that you wrote to me. Three of them I remember, in about two years.'

'I used to be moved to write them after long spells of a lonely sort of misery and dissatisfaction. Usually at night.'

'Once by moonlight – so you said.'

'Quite true; one does that sort of thing at a certain time in one's life. And your replies! Good Heavens! "I perceive in the lower corner what you would no doubt wish me to consider a tear-drop. Do not, dear lady, do not impress so honest an object as the bedroom ewer, to support these figments of the imagination."' Gallia laughed with a suspicion of sadness in the voice, sadness for those old days when such nonsense had made her so miserable. He joined in even less gleefully. Then they both said the same thing at the same moment, which often happens, but has, nevertheless, an odd enough effect.

Gallia. 'I was so fearfully in love with you, you see!'

Essex. 'You were so fearfully in love with me, you see!'

At this they laughed again.

'Well, it was that, I suppose,' Essex said; and then, looking at her, added, 'The thing has evened itself up since, hasn't it?'

She did not answer.

'Let me see the letter before you put it in.'

'No; the letter belongs to something that has no further existence.'

'And was it not the curiosity you wanted to show me?'

'No. I was the curiosity – and still am. But not of the same sort. I have repented me of the evil.'

'Why?'

'I didn't know you were going to drive Gurdon home, before. I do now: that little fact has changed my life-plan. I can't help feeling you are right to drive Gurdon home and marry him afterwards. I think he will do very well. He is really quite a fine fellow, Gurdon, and he will have all the position you care about. I know you don't care for family.'

Gallia had not interrupted any of these statements regarding her future course of action. She contented herself by saying, 'My dear Dark, *we* haven't any family ourselves. Nice, middle-class people raised to uncomfortable prominence by a vulgar title.'

'No doubt,' he assented calmly. 'Still, that's just why you might have been expected to stand out for family, you know.'

'We can do without it. Money I have in plenty. Gurdon will achieve all the position necessary for a man to have. He has the kind of talent that is indispensable to a Conservative Government. They can't get on without the keen talent of business men. Look at papa! They got in papa, in the face of enormous Cabinet opposition, to morphine the Colonies after the machinations of a Marquis. Forgive me all those silly m's. And see how it has worked. The Radicals have had to stoop and collar labour to keep *them* going, the Tories have stooped too and collared the shopkeepers – ourselves – to keep them going.'

'A facile explanation, Gallia, with as much truth in it as any woman can arrange artistically in her statements.'

'I was talking of Gurdon's position as it affects himself, not as it affects me, for it doesn't affect me. It's as a man that Gurdon appeals to me.'

'You are perfectly right,' said Essex smoothly, dusting his small, sallow hands with a handkerchief; 'he has all the manly qualities.'

'He has. He's got virility, alertness, no vague nebulous tract of country between the place where his ideas are born and the place where they are shaped for practice. He is keen and gamey and lifey. Then he's got iron self-control, a princely obstinacy, an imperial power of faithfulness.' Essex assented with his head several times. 'Added to which, he is a handsome fellow, with all the bone and muscle and blood and fibre that a man ought to have – not wasted by athletics, nor injured by slothfulness.'

'My dearest girl,' Essex said, when the list of Gurdon's virtues was full, 'he's the very man for you. Marry him. Marry him by all means!'

'I am glad you think it is all right,' said Gallia heartily. 'There's nothing in which two heads are more conspicuously better than one, than in deciding a point of this kind. The successful marriage is when you happen to want the man that other people would have chosen for you.'

'Entirely so. People have proved thousands of millions of times that it's the last move to base upon one opinion only, and that your own.'

'Well, you see why I'm going to marry him?'

'Oh, I do.'

'And I explained all my views to you before – as to what I expected to arrive at for myself?'

'You did indeed.'

'Dark, you aren't being sympathetic: what's the matter?'

'Nothing, dear.'

There was a pause, during which they sat as before, looking over to blue Sussex. Gallia's face was a little discontented.

'And now,' taking out his matchbox, 'let us burn the letter. On second thoughts, I won't let mice nibble it to pieces. Ashes are, I believe, employed as a fertiliser. Do you think a sprig of white heather would be so obliging as to spring on the grave of my hopes?'

'*Your hopes?*'

'That letter was to tell you that – Do you mind putting up your parasol? I can't get this match to light; thanks! – You see, I didn't know till now that you had decided.'

'Yes, I think I have decided.'

'Do you mind telling me, are you going to love Gurdon at all?'

'I like the "am I going to",' she laughed. 'No, Dark. The thing is not written in that key. I finished loving anyone – you know when.'

'I know when. When I began to love you.'

'Was it? Well, that was the nick of time.'

Her eyes were on the flames of the thin cream-laid note-paper of the inn.

'I would not ask to see that letter, though, of course, I would like to have seen it, just as much as you would like to have shown it me. I believe I *can* control the woman in me sometimes.'

'My dear,' Dark Essex looked up with a naïf illumination of face and a very delicate playfulness of voice, 'that's your one failing! – Now,' rising as she rose, 'shall we fly in the face of custom by not kissing each other?'

She smiled her sweetest, her most delicious smile, and walked with a graceful floating sort of swiftness over the heather. Very soon they could see the coach – the reins were just being buckled at that moment. Something had delayed the men.

'All the same,' said Gallia, turning to him and pausing, 'I think one may over-do one's sacrifices, in order to fly in the face of custom. We run the risk of giving custom too much importance.' Essex made a gesture of despair, and indeed he felt some in his heart. 'If he'd had a pinch more of the common vices of a man about him,' commented Gallia to herself, with the whimsical network showing on her forehead.

'I swear I'm so accustomed to acting as if I've no feelings, that I begin to think I haven't any!' was Essex's reflection.

Essex was a distinctly clever fellow, but he lacked a great deal of valuable common knowledge. For instance, he had never heard that there is often precious little fighting in the soldier who is too good at drill.

Chapter Twenty-Eight

'Ten miles – with plenty of hill – in fifty-four minutes.'

Gurdon took out his watch to make a calculation. They were on the level just then.

'Really, it is good! Do you think driving fast can make one hot, or is it really very warm?'

'It is warm; but you are at a certain strain to watch the road when we are going so fast, and the excitement heats you.'

'She is perfectly sure-footed, and I have never known her to stumble – but of course one must – Hullo! Aha!'

At that instant the horse had stumbled – it was only a small stumble, but Gallia pulled up immediately.

'I'll go back and see what it was.' Mark got promptly out and walked along the road; there was an inch deep of powdery sand in the track, and among it more than one rounded stone. He came back and reported, and they went on again, but Gallia's brow was knitted. The next two miles were covered much more slowly, and conversation was somewhat disjointed.

'There! I was afraid of it, she's going lame of that near fore! Never in all the four years that I have had her has she known one minute's lameness. She must have strained herself in recovering. We shall come very soon to the Noah's Ark Inn; I will stop there and rest her for half an hour.'

'We might have tea, perhaps?'

Mark knew much better than to offer to look after the horse; he went and found the ostler, however, and then he set himself to ordering tea and strawberries in a quaint little sitting-room looking out upon a garden choked with flowers.

The strain was rather more serious than she had imagined, and Gallia was about twenty minutes in getting a hot-water bandage on the leg, after having bathed it as long as the hot water of the 'Noah's Ark' – a tap which had small popularity, apparently, and was little enquired for – held out. She came in at length and described her labours.

'And I am afraid, do you know, that we must go home by train!'

'Very well. What a pity for the little horse! You will want to take him too. Shall I get a man to go to the station, and see if by any means a horse-box can be had?'

She gratefully accepted this suggestion, and Mark went to put it in force at once.

'At any rate,' she said to herself, as she arranged her hair at the oblong glass on the over-mantel – 'At any rate, he is a person of resource in little things. So tremendously necessary. He is the kind of man who would miss the last train, and arrive just the same. And one has to admire that. Whereas, poor Dark – dear, dear! how much one could love Dark for being totally without that sort of quality!'

Gurdon came in at that moment.

'It is all right; the man has gone. And I just gave him a telegram to the stationmaster at Haslemere, asking him to put a horse-box on to the 6.35 from there; so that, even if there is none at this little place, you will probably get one all the same.'

'What a useful person you are!'

Gallia looked laughingly at him. This fresh proof of his readiness in little things amused her.

'Do you dislike useful people?'

'How should I? Ah, here is tea!'

She helped the dumb, heavily-breathing country girl to spread the table, then she lifted a pot of musk from the window and put it in the centre.

What a gracious sort of thing to do! thought Mark.

They sat down. As is usual in the country, the bread was greyish and a little sour, the butter was salt and out of a tub, the jam was somebody or other's whole squashed fruit, and the tea someone else's best bonded, which recalled the delicious hay of a year ago. They had no fresh eggs, and they had no cream, and they had no water-cress. But Gurdon was in love with Gallia Hamesthwaite, so it didn't matter.

And Gallia Hamesthwaite was in love with logic, so it didn't matter.

'Ah!' he put down his cup with rapture; '*friendly* Brownie! But the Brownies belong to the good folks, don't they?'

'They do. And this time their little doings will be the means of keeping us away from our friends till eight o'clock, and making papa very anxious.'

'He surely won't be so anxious when he reflects that you are with me?' Gurdon said rather foolishly, with the carelessness of a person who is wanting to say one particular thing, and bestows the least possible attention upon any other subject that may happen to come up.

He received a look of cool enquiry from Gallia.

'He will be anxious about you too. Brownie should have taken care of both of us, and Brownie didn't.'

'Brownie has been the means of our being alone here together,' said Gurdon boldly. 'I seem never to have found you alone in my life till now.'

'Why should you have expected to? The way we all live is calculated always to bring people together in droves, not alone together.'

'But how can you get to know anyone whom you persistently meet in droves?'

'Somehow or other, even in London, you do find yourself alone with people who want to know you, and whom you want to know.' Gallia spoke musingly, the long dim cloister at Westminster rising before her eyes.

'It has never yet happened to me.'

'It has happened to you here today.'

Still there was the cloud of elsewhere in her eyes, the tentative remote tone in her voice. Mark was no psychologist, and it did not disturb him.

And He and She the banquet scene completing,
With dreamy words and very pleasant eating,*

he said contentedly, holding up a really quite presentable strawberry.

She smiled upon him.

'Something has put me in mind of a poem I once knew, I have thought of it at intervals all day. I wonder if you know it?'

'Let me hear it.'

He said it. He had a good voice; he said it very well. There is no need to detail the poem. Everybody has had such a poem in his mind on such an occasion; everybody will remember some of it. It was quite the usual poem.

'You have a great feeling for poetry,' said Gallia thoughtfully, when he had finished.

'For a practical kind of fellow, I believe music and poetry have far too much meaning for me.'

'Do you like your life salted with poetry? 'she asked, thoughtfully still.

'If I could get it,' Mark answered, smiling; 'if not, I am prepared to do without it.'

'An unusual attitude for you, Mr Gurdon.'

'Very, I admit – I'm seldom prepared to do without what I want. As you will have guessed, or someone may have told you, I am a very ambitious man.'

She laughed. 'I have guessed – and everybody has told me besides.'

'Think of the most ambitious design I could entertain – towards you, for instance.'

He had courage, but he lowered his voice and he spoke slowly, very slowly.

Gallia looked at him; her face and eyes were not unkind, and there was a gleam of playfulness in them.

'I think of it,' she said. 'And you can put it aside at once.'

He lifted his shoulders slightly, as though to get a better breath.

'I am so in earnest,' he said, with a good deal of effort. 'Gallia, I am so in earnest.' He clasped his right hand round his left, pressed them so till the white pattern of each finger was shown above each knuckle, then, still clasped, he dropped them between his knees. 'Think what I want – I want to make you my wife!'

'Now, why?' said Gallia, not flippantly but with interest. 'That's only the second most ambitious design I can think of, but tell me why?'

He missed the parenthesis, the answer to that 'why' was burning in him so hotly. He stammered his reply, seemed to reject the first part of his answer, and said, with great restraint, 'Because I admire you more than any woman I have ever seen. And because I admire you more than I could admire any woman in the world, seen or not seen.'

She looked at him critically.

'You shall tell me more of that later. It is my turn to say something. You shan't suffer the unfairness of the average proposal scene if I can help it.'

'The unfairness?'

'Yes. A man has to say all the humble, uncomfortable things – in the sweat of his brow – and a girl listens calmly and allows smiles to dawn at intervals. We won't do that. We'll try and be more honest. So it is my turn now. I have thought for some little time of marrying you, and to spare you any further anxiety, I may tell you that I had decided to if you spoke of it.'

Mark recognised the tremendous individuality of this speech, and took both her hands in a grasp of great strength, a grasp that trembled from his desire not to crush those hands too tightly.

'Gallia!' It was a cry of great joyfulness; the astonishing whiteness of his face gave way before a rush of blood. 'But you mustn't accept me yet,' he said, '– not like that. I have things to tell you, things about myself. You must know them before you say that' – he inhaled sharply, with a musical note in his breath – 'that you will take me.'

'Of course we shall have to talk about it a very great deal. But if I tell you a few things, it will save time. And we can do the talking at greater leisure.'

'That reminds me' – he seized his watch and then leapt up; 'how *dare* there be trains?' He took her hand again, even as he looked for and rang the bell. 'We must leave instantly if we are to walk Brownie to the station.'

Gallia, without another word, flew out of the room. Mark gave the girl who came half a sovereign, and followed to the stable-yard. The harness had already been stowed in the little cart. And Gallia came out of the stable leading a still limping Brownie by a borrowed halter. They set off, Mark beside her, she leading her horse.

The lane that Mark and Gallia followed seemed to lead into the heart of a lemon-and-silver evening rather than to any landward point. They were silent for a little time. Then Mark, after many inward hesitations, took her free hand and held it. The conversation, so hurriedly concluded, seemed a little difficult to take up.

'There are so many things I must tell you, so much to explain, so much to put you in possession of,' Gallia began perplexedly, as they went along, 'and this doesn't seem the occasion. This is not a serious occasion, it is a sentimental occasion'; she placed a dreadful inflection on the word sentimental, which made Gurdon apprehensive. 'This lane, the scent of those queen-of-the-meadows, the honeysuckle and roses, that sky over there above the fir trees, is too much for me; the whole thing is a stage set, and we are puppets! I can't be serious.' He listened very sympathetically. 'And the press of centuries of tradition is weighing on me and pulling and dragging me.' She shook her head and threw it up as a horse does when unused to harness. 'I can't be myself. All the dead women in the world who have done identical things at such moments are coercing me, are pushing and constraining me to act as they did. And if I do, I shan't mean it – it won't be me, it will be them – all the women who have been loved and who have gone before. What chatter it is to talk of being free, or of getting free! as if we ever could! Make her the moment and the man, and every woman takes to sentiment smiling, as a little yellow fluffy duckling flounders quacking to a pool. Oh, what chatter – what chatter it has all been, this talk of freedom! Sometimes there are moments in life when one actually sees a little further – when emotion and excitement lift one above the shoulders of the colder crowd. Free? Individually free? Poor women, if that is what we want! We undo one knot in order to be "free" to tie another. Women are like members of an Alpine party – looped each to one long rope. Even I, who have no sentiment in me, my hands and arms would know perfectly how to clasp you.'

Mark shivered with sudden passion.

'That would be instinct,' he said in a whisper.

'It would not! It would be heredity! Savage man and woman did not make love as we do, they had no instinct of that kind. You eat and hunt and kill and sleep and marry by instinct – but there is no primary instinct of love-making. It is heredity. A trick of heredity. Hands, arms, and lips are born with the cunning of it, and whether one feels like it or not has little enough to do with it.'

Mark admired her the more for this fire, though it puzzled him.

'Gallia, can't you see what a lovely thing it is, this sweet instinct in women – in all good, true women – to respond to, and to love the man who loves them.'

'No, Mark, I *can't* see it – I never could see it. It has been my misery always to see the ugly side of love and love-making. And I feel caught in a net now, a net of sentiment. No, you are not the fowler;* it isn't your fault. It's the season and the sky and the flowers, and the whole of nature's clever 'ticing-trap. Mark, *pick* me some honeysuckle, *get* me some meadowsweet – let me take Queen Nature's shilling if I must.'

In half a minute he had put a great tower of creamy, powder-headed meadowsweet into her hand, and hung a scented trail of honeysuckle about her neck and from her hat. She let him kiss her as he did this, knowing that it had to be, that the time had come for it, and verily Mark's soul was in his eyes as he looked at her.

'How gladly I would unbe everything I have ever been for you now!' he said, rather strangely, and still held her face lightly with his hands.

'I forget – have you said that you loved me?' asked Gallia.

'I don't know if I've said it. I don't think I am going to say it. There are things to tell you first. And I think, too' – he raised his arms above his head and looked up into the air and seemed to expand himself to the evening – 'I think, too, if you will allow me, I will never say it – I will live it.'

Words rose to Gallia's lips in reply, but she saw the lemon lines in the sky, and the masses of silver cloud and the bars of misty blue that would be indigo in an hour, and she smelt the flowers, and knew the dead women of the world were having their will of her, were triumphing in her. She made no answer. They were both silent. Just before they went into the station, Gurdon said tenderly –

'I owe Brownie something!' and he stopped and kissed the beast's bright neck, just above where Gallia's hand lay on it, then he kissed her hand too. 'My hand!' he said.

'Oh, dead, dead women who are so strong still!' cried Gallia in her puzzled heart. 'And dead men too, that teach so faithfully!'

'What will you do with your flowers?' said the man of the world dubiously, as they went into the station yard.

'I shall wear them,' said Gallia.

'You look lovely in them,' responded the lover, with an ecstatic modulation.

Chapter Twenty-Nine

As they sat down on the little narrow bench at the end of the horse-box, opposite Brownie's frightened head, Gallia felt the weight of the situation becoming intolerable. Never in her life had she put off the awkward moment, the moment of confession, abasement, explanation – whatever it might have been. The torments of a person with something on his mind were new to her. She had an almost endless buoyancy of soul, owing to her habit of immediate honesty. This moment now burdened her as much as had those others long ago, when it had been Essex to whom her explanation was owed.

She was silent, sometimes looking out at the blue and black evening, sometimes letting her eyes rest on Brownie's head. Mark had been silent too, by way of sympathy with her mood. Also, he had a great deal to think of. Events had hurried him somewhat; instead of all falling out decently and in order, here was only another example of Nature's or Life's lack of any sense of propriety. It deeply offended Gurdon's sense of decency to have spoken to Miss Hamesthwaite while Cara Lemuel still depended upon him for support. She would never, of course, hear of it, but Gurdon had his theories; he honoured the woman who was to be his wife; he regarded this complication as a tacit offence to her, and he, on his own part, resented it. He was the victim of it as much as she was. This made him silent too. His heart beat high at his fine fortune, but – he too had his ideal, and for the sake of an opportunity he had not acted up to it.

He chose an outside subject to break in upon their constraint.

'Imagine your coming in this box and insisting on travelling with the horse!' he said, with a kind touch in his voice.

'I would not have excused a servant for getting into a carriage and leaving a nervous horse alone,' Gallia answered simply.

'But then it would have been the servant's business.'

'It is the business of anybody who happens to be *with* a horse to look after him, isn't it? Besides, wouldn't you rather be in a carriage with a dear horse whom you know than in a carriage with tiresome people whom you instinctively hate?'

He laughed.

'Oh, far rather,' he said. 'It is said that women who are fond of animals to the extent that you are, don't care for children.'

'If children are as nice as nice animals, I like them extremely. But why should one be expected to adore other people's children, out of hand? It's absurd. Fortunately it's dying out. Now, do you like children?'

He did not answer at once; as a matter of fact, he could not command his voice. He had never had anything like this emotion to quell before – he had not believed himself capable of it – now it choked him. If he had at that moment recalled his love for Margaret – which had been a mere drawing-room feeling, with as little substance about it as a cretonne* – if he had recollected some other feelings of his in another relation, he would have shouted in their repudiation. This, this now, was his first moment of feeling; he was indeed hoisted above the shoulders of the colder crowd; he was scarce able to breathe for the tumult in his breast. Her question had been put quite lightly; she had had no *arrière pensée*;* but the instant she felt him take her hand in the spell of the silence that had fallen, and heard him breathing, she knew a moment had come.

'I shall love my own children,' he said, very low and gravely, 'if God – and you – give me any.'

Mark, the worldly-minded; Mark, the agnostic; Mark, the erect man of nowadays, whose knee had never bent at any shrine! And till then he had never known any thought that went so deeply with him; he had never cared or meant a hundredth part as seriously.

Could Gallia reply? It was her time; she was strangely moved; it must have been a sob, half of exaltation, half of regret, that he heard in her voice. If it had been Essex who was beside her, whose hand was in hers! If he had said those last words! Just in a flashing second she wondered if it would have come natural to her to reply. She looked searchingly round the box – but a little light came in at the square window, a mere fading beam, and there was no lamp. Oh, if it had been Essex! She could have told him true. She thought of her duty, she thought of her free choice, she thought of her ideals. She was strong enough then for the ordeal by fire. She belonged now to the man beside her, she had chosen to belong to him; and he was hers, she had selected him to be hers.

'I will love our child,' she said. He said nothing, he was more than happy.'

Some priest wrapped in mystic adoration, kneeling in the chequered light of the Virgin's chapel, praying for the atonement of man's sins to woman, who has felt his heart reel to that most sacred depth of humility which is the first step upon the gold stairway of pardon, might sympathise with Gurdon's feeling then.

Presently he awoke to be a man again.

'Will you not say once, now, that you love me?' he asked.

'Need we say our alphabet?' asked Gallia, with a swift change of humour, and he was sure he had made a mistake. 'Ah, yes,' she went on, 'I must tell you. I am not marrying you because I love you.'

'Then forgive me my vanity – if I took that for granted, it is because I knew of no other possible reason for your marrying me. Why, then – why are you willing to be my wife?'

'Frankly, I am not allured by the prospect of being anybody's wife,' she said, taking up her adherence to her older feelings. 'But I want to marry; and I want you to be my husband – or rather, the father of my child.'

He was puzzled and he was piqued – he did not in the least follow her.

'I do not love you – I may no doubt come to have a strong affection for you.' – He recovered a little – he was ready, as every man is ready, to undertake to teach her to love him; he was going to tell her so in a minute. 'But I admire you; you fill out my idea of what a man should be, not only in looks, but in qualities. Perhaps it seems strange to you, but I have never had much love in me, and that little I used up some time ago, on someone who did not care for me, and whom, if I had married, I should have been disappointed with now. I have only yearned to be a mother – I can't explain and say more about it than that, even to you; I have wanted the father of my child to be a fine, strong, manly man, full of health and strength. A man who is a man, whose faults are manly; who has never been better than a mere man in all his life.'

He marvelled greatly, then he said, 'But – do you know enough of my life to feel satisfied? For, Gallia, I love you. So much that you shall take me on your own terms. I shall be yours, and you shall be your own! When I cannot understand, I shall still love you. I do not quite follow you now, but with you I know that there is no single feeling but what is noble and honourable and honest. Now – you must hear about my life – I must be as honest as you would have me – as, indeed, I wish to be.'

'Thank you, Mark; as I said before, the discomfort shall not be all yours. It would have been strange if, with my views, I had agreed to marry you being ignorant of your life. An odd series of little circumstances placed me in possession of certain facts –'

'You know that I loved Margaret Essex?'

'Well, I did not. But I could not forgive any man who had not loved Margaret Essex. She is the ideal woman. She is a thousand women – not one woman. All men ought to worship her.'

He laughed, picked up her hand and kissed it. 'Looking back on it, it seems very curious,' he said; 'she touched none of the chords you touch in me. Every fibre in me loves you!' His voice was warm and joyous again. 'So what did you know?' He had no suspicion of what was coming.

'Well, I believe I was already dreaming of marrying you – possibly, and if you would have me – when the knowledge of the illness of your mistress came to my ears.'

If a cannon had gone off close to his head, Mark would have been less amazed.

'You will believe that I was not prying into your life,' said Gallia judicially, not as one asking a question, but as one giving an order. He was too astounded to speak. Could Essex, who just possibly might know something of it, have – but never, never, never – that was wholly impossible.

She recapitulated the chain of events that had put her in possession of these facts, and still Mark's silence held good.

'I went down into the country to think things over, to review my life, and be quite sure of what I wanted to do with it. At first – just at first, Mark – I did not like it; it somehow – did not please me. I will not go into the reasons, though I think I know them all now. Then – I saw that I must reform my thoughts; I saw that the logical sequence of my views about the kind of man I wanted to marry read equally as my approval –'

'Don't, Gallia! For God's sake, don't, don't, don't!' Without knowing why, Mark knew that he could not bear this. He could bear the rest, but this he simply *could not bear*. It was the agony of knives to him.

There was a pause; in Gallia's brain an explanation of his feeling made itself heard. Throughout the ages, a man's wife is expected to disapprove of his mistress while she forgives him for having one; all this is tacit. It is impossible for a man to listen to his adored wife talking – in no matter what fashion – of his previously cherished mistress. That this is as incomprehensible as the number of physical elements, matters nothing. It is so.

'Would you rather have me angry with you about it?' asked Gallia.

'Infinitely rather,' said Gurdon; 'it would be more natural.'

'If I loved you, I might be jealous of her,' thought she, but wisely said nothing.

'Well, you cannot get over the fact that it was owing to my hearing of her at the time and in the way that I did, that decided me to marry you.'

Gallia clasped her hands round her knees and looked disconsolately before her.

Gurdon groaned. The longest pause of all occurred.

Gallia abandoned Gurdon, his head in his hands, and occupied herself with Brownie.

In the meantime the train drew into the station. They roused themselves, and the horse was got out and a man found to take it to the Hall.

'I find they can have a fly from the inn in a few minutes.'

'Very well. I am going to walk. I should prefer it.'

This sounded as though Mark was to have the privilege of driving alone in the fly; he could not believe that she meant it.

'If you wish to walk, I am very willing; but are you not tired?'

'Not the least. I'm made of better stuff. I want to walk because I want to think. You had better think too. I see I have frightened you. You had never seen the real me till now, and you don't like her. Very well. Let her go – there is no harm done.'

'Hush! hush! Life is not a child's game, Gallia.'

'No,' she murmured, with a wry smile; 'it is too dull for that.'

They had been walking down the ash-path, now Gallia led the way to a short cut through the wood which cut off the hill. He put his arm round her and they walked silently on. After all, he thought, there isn't another woman alive who could regard such affairs as calmly, or with so complete an absence of hysteria. And he was going to teach her to love him. Things seemed to point very naturally to his asking her to forgive him. This is not at all an unusual way for things to point, in the early stages of a love episode – later, the woman has to ask forgiveness.

'It is to be as you please – you shall take me for whatever you please, no matter in what capacity, for better or for worse. I – I am proud that you want me.'

It was really rather fine in Mark.

'Perhaps you will learn to have some little feeling for me – some day.'

This rather astonished Gallia, who was, as a rule, occupied singly with her own life and her own future, feeling these to be as much as she could manage.

'It would disappoint me very greatly in myself,' she said, very naïvely, 'if I came to love you.'

Mark laughed. Somehow this intoxicated him. He took her in his arms and crushed her till he frightened her. Being only a simple young woman after all, this had a great effect upon her. If only Essex had had the grit to go as far – to laugh and go as far.

Chapter Thirty

There were signs of commotion in the house when Gallia and Gurdon walked into the hall about nine o'clock – commotion of a regulated and decently-constrained nature, as became a large and well-managed house, but nevertheless commotion.

Gallia's eye fell on a copy of the *Figaro* of that day's date on one of the hall tables, and, with a confused idea in her mind, she left Gurdon and ran along the flagged terrace upon which the windows of the drawing-rooms opened.

Upon so hot an evening as it was, none were closed.

'Aunt Celia!' she exclaimed, in great excitement – 'well?' – bursting into the room. 'When I saw the *Figaro* – Yes, papa, perfectly sound and unhurt! Brownie fell lame, so we came home by train. Forgive my not welcoming you except by an Indian warwhoop. I am so glad to see you, Aunt Celia, for, of course, it means you are better.' She came over to the armchair in which Mrs Leighton, still in her bonnet and slowly peeling off outer wisps of wholly unprotective laces, had evidently not long sat down.

'I was well enough to escape, dear, and I have come here to recover, if you will let me, from the severities of the cure. They have tried me inexpressibly.' She shut her eyes, raised her eyebrows, and, with a slight trembling of the delicate ivory and lavender-veined lids, inhaled whiffs of strong ammonia from a bottle.

Gallia had the good taste not to exclaim upon her improved appearance, for nothing would have offended the old lady more than any remark of the kind, but she was, in point of fact, looking wonderfully better.

Just as Gallia finished a somewhat fuller explanation of the accident, Gurdon, who had changed his clothes, came into the room. A servant had apprised him of Mrs Leighton's arrival, and Gallia could not withhold her admiration of his greeting of her. The homage of her favourite young man threw a great sparkle into the old lady's face, and even to the orange ribbon in her charming bonnet, she seemed to brighten.

'Your rooms, dear Aunt Celia –'

'Thank you, child, I will go upstairs after I have had my bouillon; oh, here it comes! Of course I have brought my own sheets – I have given up camel's hair and am sleeping in pine wool* now. No sheet can be fit to use unless it has been aired for forty-eight hours consecutively.' Mrs Leighton spoke with authority; she was in the habit of changing the material of her sheets in a sweeping fashion about every three months, and invariably carried the latest fad to her friends' houses when she visited.

'Thank you, Gerald,' as Lord Hamesthwaite's arm came to her assistance in leaving the room. 'You will tell me your fortunes tomorrow?' This to Mark, who was opening the door.

'I am coming up with you to see that you have everything,' said Gallia, whose cheek was flushing faintly, even as was Mark's.

But there were no confidences of any sort that night, and, greatly wearied by her own affairs, and the perplexity that these had brought her, Gallia sent messages downstairs to her guests, and shut herself into her own rooms for the night.

A night's rest is supposed to have a chemical effect on most situations; in the morning light difficulties are said to appear more surmountable. Gallia, however, was not conscious of having difficulties exactly; to act in accordance with a plan is not necessarily to make things easier for the people with whom you act, but for the actor it greatly lightens the task of living.

Gallia, all her life long, had acted in accordance with sets of preconceived ideas; with her growth these had either strengthened or modified, but in some form or other they were always there.

Instinct, as will have been seen, had no place in deciding her actions; nor, in a certain sense, could intuition have had much force with her. Some people, whose minds have been trained in religion, will do what they think God would have them do – that is, what they believe to be right. Gallia, who had no religious ideas, and had never at any moment in her life felt the want of any, was only anxious to do what was honest and honourable.

If a given movement were fair and just to others, then it was the one that she would take; and upon such points she examined herself rigorously from time to time, and raised her standard always a little bit higher.

Before breakfast next morning she had an interview with her father, of a quite satisfactory kind; to him she naturally wished to confide her feelings towards Gurdon at once, and take his advice about announcing her engagement. Lord Hamesthwaite had nothing but what was favourable to say. He was not an ambitious man, but even if he were, he felt he might have had reason to be satisfied with Mark.

In Brownie's loose-box she found Gurdon, whom she sent straightway to her father's room.

Margaret and Robbie she found upon the terrace.

'I absolutely repudiate the idea that that picnic in any way assisted *me*,' Robbie was saying, in answer to some badinage from Gertrude. 'I have been engaged to Margaret for about two years.'

'How one does dread proposals!' Miss Janion said fervently. 'They are so samey and they are *so* dull. There is something frightful in sitting beside a man and *knowing* he is trying to lead up to a proposal. And when he *has* led up to it! I can sit and say with my lips every succeeding sentence – you know, as one does some of the prayers in church. There's a system, and he never departs from it. He always has to go into his past. Have you noticed what a passion men have for telling girls about their pasts? They are so proud of their blundering, unimaginative records – and, of course, every girl must think how far better she could have done it. Men are like children who have come home from the seashore.' She fixed a bright magnetic eye upon Lord Shillinglee, who appeared in the distance, and drew him to the spot. 'They have to tell about how they paddled, and just how deep they went in, and all about the queer things they fished out, and about the crabs that caught hold of their toes.' Everybody had to laugh at this bit of Gertrude's description, though Margaret was blushing like a nectarine. 'And all the time you see how awfully frightened at the crabs they have been. "But our little shoes were hanging round our necks, Nursey dear",' – here she imitated the small, high voice of the self-consciously good child – 'they say, as they put them on again. "And see how clean we've kept our overalls!"'

Robbie dissolved in a perfect paroxysm of laughter.

'It will require enormous nerve to put a man off this confession, they so love to be forgiven; it will be depriving him of a sacred moment; but the man I marry will have to be generous and make the sacrifice. I have heard the detailed pasts of so many men, it will be quite refreshing to know nothing of my husband's.'

While the young people babbled and laughed together, Mrs Leighton's maid had been busily erecting a large square umbrella of cream-coloured muslin, bordered with engaging frills, and lined with pink; beneath this had been placed a comfortable chair. To this bower Mark now escorted the old lady, and they fell into earnest conversation. Mark could not detail his fortune without Gallia's permission, but the skilful diplomatist, who had liked and encouraged him from the first, put certain astute questions, and drew her own conclusions from the guarded replies. Fortunately, the state of affairs which she suspected pleased her greatly. Robbie's engagement to Margaret had put her in a good temper, and she soon dispelled a slight sense of regret that Gallia was not to marry a man of old family – old family being a thing that she had always declared her dislike of, publicly.

She would have been angry if it had been Essex, and she was always rather frightened that it might be Essex. Yet there was Essex, his clothes having been fetched for the night from Hiddenfold – there was Essex looking vaguely out over the park. When Gurdon joined Gallia, Mrs Leighton summoned Hubert.

She put a number of quite barefaced questions to him, about his career and prospects and intentions. With people whom she believed to be unimportant, she could behave in a mildly unscrupulous manner that was surprising. Finesse, she argued, should never be thrown away.

'Marriage?' said Dark speculatively, when he had been led to the block. 'A man with pronounced heart-disease ought not to marry. Nothing is more inevitably hereditary. No,' smiling at her faintly, 'I never contemplated marriage.'

'Funny!' the old lady was left murmuring; 'everybody has insisted on Gallia being consistent, and makes no allowance for a possible reversion to the type; she has acted in accordance with her absurd opinions, because her heart has never awakened to scatter her reason. She will fall in love with that attractive manifestation of heart-disease yet. But she will be married, so it will not signify.'

Mrs Leighton was not very far out here, and would not have been so far out, had she had more leisure to observe Gallia and Essex together, and know that her prophecy had come true already. The wind grew a little too strong, and she sauntered indoors for more shelter.

'Essex, I want a word with you.' Gurdon came up and put a hand on Dark's arm; 'Shall we go into the smoking-room? There is no one there.'

Not especially wondering what Mark could have to say to him, Essex followed into the smoking-room with a leisurely step. When he came out three-quarters of an hour later, his face moved unconsciously; his old well-accustomed smile struggled to play over it.

'You see, with Denyer on the spot, and things at their present juncture, I cannot possibly leave here,' Gurdon was saying as they walked out together.

Essex nodded once or twice, and went on up the stairs alone to Gallia's study.

'I am just leaving,' he said, 'and heard that you were here.'

'You are going away now?'

'Yes; the atmosphere is becoming somewhat overcharged with sentiment; besides, I ought to be going back to work.'

'Do you know,' she said, observing him very closely, 'you look ill.'

'Do I?'

'Pale. You do really! A curious pallor. Is your heart all right, Dark?'

'Bust up in my rowing days, I believe, but it will last my time.'

'Why did you never tell me?' she asked, with a sense of having been shut out from his confidence.

'Had I not enough disadvantages in your eyes, without that?'

Gallia coloured very deeply and painfully.

'I should only have mentioned it to you in one event.'

'And that?'

'Well, we needn't mind that now. Heart-disease, you know, is hereditary.'

A curious light came into Gallia's eyes – she understood him.

'Goodbye. We shan't meet again for some little time, I think. When does your marriage take place?'

'Oh, no date has been spoken of yet.'

'Ah, well, I shall see you then.'

'I don't think I want you to come.'

'Really? Just as you wish. I would like to have seen you looking dreadfully beautiful. But you won't banish me afterwards altogether?'

'Oh no. Besides, Mark looks upon you as a friend.'

Essex rose and held out his hand, and his smiling eyes met hers.

'He has some little reason to,' he said quietly, and was gone.

In a quarter of an hour he was walking to the station.

'I shall get to the junction in time for the 2.15 to Brighton,' he said, 'and then I can do my last service to Gallia. The first, she said, was burying the letter. The second will be Gurdon's commission to Miss Lemuel. Fate has at any rate a redeeming sense of humour.'

NOTES

---

p. iii title-page epigraph: Hans Christian Andersen's *The Marsh-King's Daughter* was first translated into English in 1890. See Introduction, pp. xl.

p. xliv dedication χάλκεα χρυσείων: literally, 'Bronze things for gold ones'. More poetically, 'Bronze returns for gifts of gold'. Dowie's husband, Henry Norman, had discovered gold-mines in Asia, so the dedication is affectionately witty.

p. 4 *rusée*: wily.

p. 4 *'tout comprendre'*: a reference to the proverbial phrase 'tout comprendre, c'est tout pardonner', to understand everything is to forgive everything. Possibly also an allusion to the much quoted line from Mme. de Stael's *Corinne*: 'Tout comprendre rend très indulgent', to be totally understanding makes one very indulgent.

p. 4 Kümmel: carraway flavoured liqueur.

p. 5 *grille, entresol, grenier,* and *sous le toit*: gateway, basement, attic and loft.

p. 6 *plein air*: fresh air.

p. 6 *fleur de limon:* lime-flower.

p. 7 *poste-télégraphe*: telegram.

p. 7 Passage des Favorites: Dowie presumably means the Rue des Favorites, which adjoins the Rue de Vaugirard. See note to p. 11.

p. 7 Lille et d'Albion in the Rue de Rivoli: actually in the Rue St Honoré. The Lille et d'Albion was one of the larger hotels in Paris, and much frequented by English visitors.

p. 7 Latin Quarter: the site of the Sorbonne University and several of Paris's government buildings, and of many artists' studios. A centre of bohemianism.

p. 7   **serge:** thick wool jacket or coat.

p. 7   **crush hat:** collapsible hat.

p. 9   *Petit Caporal*: inferior grade tobacco. 'Petit Caporal' was the nickname given to Napoleon I by his soldiers.

p. 9   **Rue Vaugirard:** inhabited, in the 1890s, primarily by families with moderate incomes, especially shopkeepers and artisans. It contained numerous market gardens.

p. 9   **Bulliers:** the Bal Bullier, or Closerie des Lilas, in the Quartier Latin, was a popular bohemian haunt. Baedecker's 1891 guide to *Paris and Environs* noted that 'the dancing of students and artisans with their "étudiantes" or "ouvrières"' here was 'generally of a wild and Bacchanalian character'. It was advertised as one of the places at which the English visitor to Paris might expect to see the cancan danced.

p. 9   **the Divan Japonais and the Alcazar:** seedier nightclubs. The Alcazar was in the Faubourg-Montmartre.

p. 11   **Favorites:** the 'favorites' were the King's preferred mistresses.

p. 11   *barrière*: the gates of the old city. In this case, the *barrière Vaugirard*.

p. 13   **'J'amène... pas':** loosely, 'I have brought a friend of mine, darling, but don't let it put you out.'

p. 13   **'Tiens ... manger!':** 'Fine – so long as he does not want to eat!'

p. 14   *casserole*: saucepan.

p. 14   *fourneau*: oven.

p. 14   **Mi-Carême:** mid-Lent.

p. 14   *croquis*: sketches.

p. 18   **Français:** the Théâtre Français.

p. 19   **the Franco-German question:** the ongoing dispute over Alsace-Lorraine. The region was under Prussian control from 1871 to 1918, a fact more or less hotly contested throughout that period.

p. 19   **numbers:** exam marks.

p. 21   **Auteuil:** reunited with Paris in 1860, the Auteuil was still a quiet suburban district at the end of the nineteenth century, and a favourite haunt of writers. The racetrack (the Champ de Courses d'Auteuil) was built in the 1870s on the south side of the old park. Races and steeple chases took place in the spring and autumn.

p. 21 'team down': *i.e.* team up.

p. 21 the rights and wrongs of the Swazis: Great Britain had extended protection to Tongaland in 1888, after Boer farmers, prospectors and concessioners set up the 'Little Free State' in breach of the London convention of 1883. Swaziland was annexed to the Transvaal in 1894, subject to guarantees of native rights, but close relations continued between the Swazi people and Great Britain during the Boer War (1899–1902). Swaziland became a British protectorate in 1906.

p. 22 Jardin du Luxembourg: described in Baedecker's 1891 guide to Paris as the only remaining Renaissance garden in Paris.

p. 22 Hôtel Foyot: in the Rue de Tournon near the Palais de Luxembourg. Frequented by the clergy.

p. 25 Munkacszy: Mihály (Michael) von Munkácsy (1844–1900). Hungarian-born painter, who lived and made his reputation primarily in Paris. He specialised in large-scale genre paintings similar in style to those of Courbet, including *The Last Day of the Prisoner Condemned to Death* (1870) and *The Blind Milton Dictating Paradise Lost* (1878).

p. 25 Laurent: a mistake for Jean-Paul Laurens (1838–1921) who designed some of the murals in the Panthéon and in the Hôtel de Ville de Paris.

p. 25 Amer Picon: a bitter herbal liqueur.

p. 28 Cluny and Panthéon: the Musée de Cluny held a valuable collection of medieval art objects and products of industry; Leighton would probably have been interested in the Panthéon primarily because of Laurens's 'The Death of Ste. Geneviève'. See second note to p. 25.

p. 29 *ouvriers*: workmen.

p. 29 *Marmorweib*: the marble woman.

p. 31 Gallia: apparently a feminine form of 'Gallio'. Lucius Annaeus Gallio was the brother of the philosopher Seneca, and proconsul of Achaea *c.* 52 AD. He is remembered primarily for his refusal to hear the

Jews' case against St Paul. When the Greeks brought the chief ruler of the synagogue before him for judgement, he again refused to intervene (see Acts xviii: 12–17). His name became a byword for indifference to public opinion. Several of Seneca's works were dedicated to him, and he later became consul, but he was compelled to take his own life after his brother's disgrace and suicide.

p. 32 *Dieu soit béni*: (loosely) thank God.

p. 33 **an agitation about the State regulation of vice**: the Contagious Diseases Acts of 1864, 1866 and 1869 were introduced in an attempt to reduce the incidence of syphilis among military men. They allowed the police in garrison towns to arrest any woman on suspicion of prostitution and force her to undergo a medical examination. The assumption that women, rather than the men they slept with, were the source of venereal disease caused an outcry. The campaign against the acts, led by Josephine Butler, was soon difficult to ignore, and public debate about the issue gathered momentum over the next two decades. Gallia's forthright attitude is typical of the loss of innocence many public moralists mourned in the young women of the 1890s.

p. 37 *Ay de mi!*: woe is me.

p. 37 **victoria**: a light, low, four-wheeled carriage with collapsible hood, normally seating two passengers, and with a raised platform in front for the driver.

p. 38 **some misty peak in Darien**: an allusion to the last line of Keats's 'On First Looking into Chapman's Homer' – 'Silent, upon a peak in Darien'.

p. 39 **a freelance at Oxford**: *i.e.* attending lectures and following a course of study without being enrolled for a degree.

p. 44 **Stanley**: Sir Henry Morton Stanley. British explorer, famous for his discoveries in the Congo region, and for his rescue of the Scottish missionary and explorer Richard Livingstone. Stanley charted the Congo on his 1874–7 expedition. In the year *Gallia* was published, he was elected Liberal MP for North Lambeth.

p. 46 **Rosebery**: Archibald Philip Primrose, 5th Earl of Rosebery (1847–1929). Liberal politician and later Prime Minister. He assisted Gladstone to victory in the 1880 general election. He was Gladstone's

Under-Secretary of State in the Home Office from 1881–83. In 1886, and again from 1892–4, he was Secretary of State for Foreign Affairs.

p. 48 The veil of the temple was rent in twain: Matthew xxvii:51, describing the aftermath of the death of Jesus.

p. 48 'Never happy any more': the repeated first line from Dante Gabriel Rossetti, 'The Lady's Lament':

> Never happy any more!
> Aye, turn the saying o'er and o'er,
> It says but what it said before,
> And heart and life are just as sore.

p. 59 . . .put out my soul's little light: possibly an allusion to *Othello*, V.ii.6–7

> *Oth.* Yet she must die, else she'll betray more men.
> Put out the light, and then put out the light.

p. 62 the Reform: the Reform Club was founded in 1836 as a congenial meeting place for Liberal statesmen and writers. Dinners were given for distinguished non-members, and on a smaller scale for fellow members or visitors, but grand dinners were almost always for politicians. In the early 1890s, the Club was feeling the tensions produced by the Liberal split over Home Rule in Ireland.

p. 64 Greek handwriting: probably indicates that Essex draws his 'e's like Greek 'ε's.

p. 69 'road-car': bus.

p. 69 wood pavement: pavements laid out in large wooden blocks, like parquet.

p. 69 pole: attaching the horses' harness to the road car.

p. 70 *il faut cligner les yeux*: it is necessary to narrow your eyes.

p. 74 'Schlummerlied': lullaby – probably Brahms.

p. 80 opoponax: gum resin obtained from *Balsamdendron Kataf*. Used in perfumery.

p. 82 the dens: drinking haunts, probably unlicensed.

p. 83   *hôtel meublé*: a hotel which offers furnished lodgings on long leases.

p. 83   artists' colourman's: his supplier of watercolours and oils.

p. 83   *Académies:* life-studies.

p. 87   **Ah, the throats of thunder... finger-tips:** William Watson's 'The Keyboard'. The original has 'O the throats of thunder'.

p. 95   *tristesse* and *ennui*: sadness and lethargy – in this case presumably contracted from novel-reading.

p. 96   *Mademoiselle met?*: 'Mademoiselle will put on [which dress]?'

p. 96   *Celle de soie*: the silk one.

p. 96   *Celui en velours*: the velvet one.

p. 97   the very Louis: Louis XIV, XV, and XVI.

p. 97   'Salon Trianon': Marie-Antoinette's salon in the Petit Trianon at Versailles.

p. 98   Herbert Spencer: (1820–1903), philosopher and evolutionary theorist. Vigorous proponent of social and economic *laissez faire* in his early works. Gallia's theories are more evidently indebted to his later writings on individualism.

p. 99   portière: heavy curtain over the door.

p. 100   Gaboriau: Emile Gaboriau (1832–73). French novelist, sometimes credited with inventing the detective novel. Author of *L'Affaire Lerouge*, and *Monsieur Lecoq*.

p. 100   F. W. Robinson: Frederic William Robinson (1830–1901). Prolific writer. Author of approximately fifty novels, and founder and editor of *Home Chimes*.

p. 101   siskins: small song-birds, not unlike gold-finches.

p. 105   Félix or of Worth: leading Paris fashion houses.

p. 106   Przevalsky: Nikolay Mikhaylovich Prhevalsky (1839–88), Russian explorer. He travelled extensively through east central Asia. Among his natural history discoveries was the wild horse which became known as Przewalski's horse (*Equus caballus przewalskii*).

p. 107 Mrs Tree: Helen Maud Tree (1863–1937), *née* Holt. Actress, and wife of Herbert Beerbohm Tree. Remembered principally as a comic actress who excelled at Shakespeare and Sheridan. She played in many of her husband's lavish productions at His Majesty's Theatre.

p. 109 *The Comparison of Emotion in the Human and other Animals:* the title of Essex's monograph alludes to Charles Darwin's *The Expression of the Emotions in Man and Animals* (1872).

p. 110 silver-point: a drawing in silver pencil on specially prepared paper.

p. 112 galvaniser: therapist skilled in applying galvanic electricity to stimulate the muscles.

p. 115 'Sexual Revolt': a term frequently employed by newspapers and journals at the time to describe the behaviour of the new woman.

p. 118 'some Tory leopard, lay down with the Radical kid: a playful reference to Isaiah lxv:25.

p. 118 Pullman: railway sleeping-car, named after its American inventor.

p. 120 Blue Book: an official parliamentary publication (named for the regulation blue cover).

p. 120 Board Schools: a state school administered by a School Board. The Board Schools were often built in groups in the more densely populated areas of the London suburbs in order to keep expenses down. They catered for the poorest children brought into the system with the introductiion of compulsory education in 1870.

p. 123 Holland House: built in Kensington in the late seventeenth century, Holland House was the last of the great estates in London. It became famous under the 3rd Lord Holland as a centre for political, literary and social meetings of the Whig aristocracy. Lady Holland, widow of the last Lord Holland, died in 1889 and bequeathed the house to the 5th Lord Ilchester. He restored it in 1890, and in 1891 Lady Ilchester gave her first large entertainment: a masked ball. During the 1890s, Lady Ilchester made the house once again a venue for fashionable events. Her gatherings were 'exclusive and honoured by royalty, but they were no longer particularly cosmopolitan or political'

(Derek Hudson, *History of Holland House*). The house was largely destroyed by bombing in 1940.

p. 127   *entrain*: spirit, liveliness.

p. 130   the green fig-tree: in Matthew xxi:19, Christ finds a green fig tree without any fruit on it and curses it, 'Let no fruit grow on thee henceforward for ever.' The tree withers away. Gallia's rather raw point is that though Essex does not love her, she need not be without children.

p. 131   *mauvaise honte*: false shame.

p. 132   undiscovered country: *i.e.* death. An allusion to Hamlet's 'To be or not to be' soliloquy (III.i.77–81):

> the dread of something after death,
> The undiscover'd country, from whose bourn
> No traveller returns, puzzles the will,
> And makes us rather bear those ills we have,
> Than fly to others that we know not of . . .

p. 134   picked her aloe-flower: has had her one moment of love. The aloe was popularly believed to flower only once in a hundred years, and was sometimes used as an exotic metaphor for love. See, for example, P. J. Bailey's *Festus* (1839): 'there are some hearts, aloe-like, flower once and die'.

p. 147   fiddle-headed: fiddle-shaped head, possibly with the added implication of 'empty-headed'.

p. 150   shandy-gaff: bitter-ale or beer mixed with ginger-beer.

p. 157   *Tout au contraire*: quite the contrary.

p. 161   van: a movable, covered lecturing platform.

p. 163   *affairée*: busy.

p. 167   *lisse*: a fine silk gauze.

p. 168   *aguardiénte*: an inferior Spanish or Portuguese brandy; or, any cheap distilled liquor.

p. 169   *cuvée*: literally 'vatful'. In this case, a 'brew' or 'concoction' of fashionable words or phrases.

p. 177   **cubs:** unpolished young men; Essex is presumably referring to his undergraduates.

p. 183   **And He and She . . . eating:** unidentified.

p. 187   **the fowler:** predator. Usually one who hunts wild fowl for sport; but the term had acquired a particular association with sexual predation and violence. For a roughly contemporary example, see Beatrice Harraden's sensational novel, *The Fowler* (1899).

p. 190   **cretonne:** fairly hard-wearing cotton fabric, often used for upholstery.

p. 190   *arrière pensée*: literally 'backward thought'; suppressed or hidden thoughts.

p. 197   **pine wool:** downy fibre taken from under the bark of pine trees.

SUGGESTIONS FOR FURTHER READING

Although Ménie Muriel Dowie has attracted brief discussion in a few recent works on New Woman fiction, almost nothing of any length has been written about her life and works. The Introduction to this volume is the most extensive discussion of her to date and is based on new research. The following books are important for a consideration of Dowie's context within New Woman fiction of the 1890s. The titles by Ann Ardis, Kate Flint and, particularly, Gail Cunningham discuss Dowie directly:

Ann L. Ardis, *New Women, New Novels: Feminism and Early Modernism* (New Brunswick: Rutgers University Press, 1990)

Ruth Brandon, *The New Women and the Old Men: Love, Sex and the Woman Question* (London: Secker & Warburg, 1990)

Gail Cunningham, *The New Woman and the Victorian Novel* (London: The Macmillan Press, 1978)

Kate Flint, *The Woman Reader, 1837–1914* (Oxford: Clarendon Press, 1993)

Lyn Pykett, *The 'Improper' Feminine: The Women's Sensation Novel and the New Woman Writing* (London: Routledge, 1992)

Elaine Showalter, *A Literature of Their Own: British Women Novelists from Brontë to Lessing* (Princeton, NJ: Princeton, 1977)

Elaine Showalter, *Sexual Anarchy: Gender and Culture at the 'Fin de Siècle'* (London: Bloomsbury, 1991)

Patricia Stubbs, *Women and Fiction: Feminism and the Novel, 1880–1920* (Totowa, NJ: Barnes & Noble, 1979)

BIBLIOGRAPHY OF DOWIE'S WORKS

Books

A Girl in the Karpathians (London: G. Philip & Son, 1891)
2nd edn (London: G. Philip & Son, 1891)
3rd edn (London: G. Philip & Son, 1891)
4th edn (London: G. Philip & Son, 1891). Published under her married name, 'Ménie Muriel Norman'
5th edn (London: G. Philip & Son, 1892). Published under her married name, 'Ménie Muriel Norman'
(New York: Cassell Publishing Co., 1891)
2nd American edn (New York: Cassell Publishing Co., 1891)
3rd American edn (New York: Cassell Publishing Co., 1891)
4th American edn (New York: Cassell Publishing Co., 1891)
4th American edn rpt (New York: The Mershon Co., n.d.)
(Leipzig: B. Tauchnitz, 1891)

Women Adventurers. Edited by Ménie Muriel Dowie, Author of 'A Girl in the Karpathians': The Lives of Madame Velazguez, Hannah Snell, Mary Anne Talbot, and Mrs Christian Davies (London: T. Fisher Unwin, 1893)

Gallia (London: Methuen & Co., 1895)
2nd edn (London: Methuen, 1895)
(Philadelphia: J. B. Lippincott Co., 1895)

Some Whims of Fate (New York & London: J. Lane, 1896)
(London: Grant Richards, 1897)

The Crook of the Bough (London: Methuen & Co., 1898)
(New York: C. Scribner's Sons, 1898)

Love and His Mask (London: William Heinemann, 1901)

Things about Our Neighbourhood (London: Grant Richards, 1903)

Short Stories

'The Hint O'Hairst', serialised in *Chambers's Journal of Popular Literature, Science, and Art* 10 (February 1893), 73–6, 88–91, 104–8, 119–22

'Wladislaw's Lament', *The Yellow Book* 4 (January 1895), 90–115

'An Idyll in Millinery', *The Yellow Book* 10 (July 1896), 24–53

Journalism

'In Ruthenia', *Fortnightly Review* n.s. 48 (1890), 520–30

'A Talk with a Brave Woman', incorporated in [Henry Norman], 'Round the Near East: xv', *The Daily Chronicle*, 18 November 1895, p. 5

'In the Haunted Crimea', *Contemporary Review* 78 (July 1900), 38–57

'Things about Our Neighbourhood' series, *Country Life* 21 December 1901–22 November 1902

Various anonymous contributions to *The Daily Chronicle* and other newspapers and journals during the 1890s, primarily on women's issues. Unidentified.

TEXT SUMMARY

Chapter One

Mark Gurdon pays a visit to the grandmother of an old college friend, Robert Leighton. When she expresses an anxiety about how Robert is faring as a student of art in Paris, Gurdon agrees to call on him: he is eager to make a good impression on Mrs Leighton, whose contacts in the Colonial Secretary's Office may be of use to him in the future.

Chapter Two

In Paris, Gurdon meets Robert Leighton at a public studio, and is introduced to an aging English model, Lemuel. Leighton invites Gurdon back to his studio.

Chapter Three

Gurdon finds that Mrs Leighton's supposedly exaggerated fears about the Bohemian life her grandson is leading are entirely accurate. Leighton's housekeeper is also his model and his mistress; and curled up on the sofa is Lemuel's daughter. She severely shakes Gurdon's English composure by kissing him on the lips, and behaving with bizarre exuberance throughout dinner.

Chapter Four

Most of the chapter describes Mark Gurdon's background and his character. None of his life experiences to date have prepared him for being kissed by a French minx.

Chapter Five

Gurdon witnesses as Robert Leighton is publicly snubbed by a beautiful English girl, Margaret Essex. He warns Leighton that he is damaging his reputation by leading an openly bohemian lifestyle. Gurdon meets Lemuel again, and takes him for a drink. As Lemuel reveals his background, Gurdon is disturbed to find that the artist's model was formerly, like himself, a junior member of the Civil Service.

Chapter Six

Back in England, Lady Hamesthwaite, wife of the Colonial Secretary, is not in good health, and is being visited by her half sister and close friend, Mrs Leighton. They are joined by the Hamesthwaites' daughter, Gallia. Gallia espouses unladylike views about the state regulation of prostitution, currently under debate in the journals. A long account of Gallia's unorthodox upbringing, her passion for Mill and Spencer, her resistance to conventional ideas of feminine behaviour, and a hint of future unhappiness occupy the remainder of the chapter.

Chapter Seven

At a dinner party given by Mrs Leighton, Gallia meets an old Oxford acquaintance: a fellow of Balliol, known to his friends as Dark Essex, who warns her not to fall in love with him. It becomes apparent that Gallia is indeed in love with Essex, though she does not yet know it herself. She longs for him to kiss her. Instead, he roughly informs her that his life has no need of her. She drives home, desolate.

Chapter Eight

Five weeks later, Gallia has not recovered from the pain of rejection or – more cuttingly – the knowledge that she has been guilty of 'vulgar reticence'. When Essex calls to return a book, she takes the opportunity to address him frankly. She informs him that she loves him, and, though she fully accepts that he does not return her feelings, she wants his forgiveness for the flagrant immodesty with which she 'sat there and said nothing' instead of telling him honestly what she felt.

Chapter Nine
Essex is briefly thrown off balance by this remarkable show of candour, but 'priggishness and affectation' intervene to prevent him declaring his love for Gallia. Alone again, Gallia struggles with her feelings, and cannot subdue the wish that Essex had given her one 'love-kiss' before leaving her. When she rejoins her parents, she learns that she has just missed a visit from Mark Gurdon. Lady Hamesthwaite is so clearly unwell that her husband insists that she go abroad at once. Gallia readily agrees to accompany her mother to Algiers.

Chapter Ten
Lady Hamesthwaite calls on her half-sister, Mrs Leighton, to announce her departure for Algiers. She interrupts a luncheon party at which both Margaret Essex and Mark Gurdon are present. Gurdon is bewitched by Margaret. Leaving Mrs Leighton and Lady Hamesthwaite, Gurdon accompanies Margaret on the omnibus back to her home in Hammersmith, on the pretence of wanting to renew his acquaintance with Dark Essex.

Chapter Eleven
Gurdon quickly establishes himself as a friend of Dark Essex and a regular guest of the Essex family. Gurdon is in love with Margaret. At the end of the chapter he proposes, only to be kindly but firmly rejected.

Chapter Twelve
Mark accepts his rejection. He tries various distractions without much benefit, until he meets Miss Lemuel in distress in Piccadilly late one night. Her father has come to London to pose for an English painter. He is supposed to be finding accommodation for them both, but she suspects that he is spending his money on drink. Gurdon hires a cab, and solicitously accompanies her to the apartment where she has temporarily left her belongings.

Chapter Thirteen
Cara Lemuel bursts into tears. Mark Gurdon comforts her, and one thing leads to another.

Chapter Fourteen
In Algiers, Lady Hamesthwaite has died. Gallia sits beside the body, waiting for the arrival of her father from England.

Chapter Fifteen
After two months in the Alpes Maritimes, Gallia returns to England. On a visit to her aunt, she meets Margaret Essex, and is intrigued by her. She asks Margaret to visit her. As Gallia leaves the house, she is seen by Mark Gurdon, just arriving, who thinks her 'a magnificent girl'.

Chapter Sixteen
Gurdon rents a studio in a quiet Kensington square, and establishes Cara Lemuel in it. She is now his kept mistress, and – in addition to other favours – entertains him with Spanish songs and dancing. Gurdon leads a bohemian private life similar to that of Leighton, but, unlike Leighton, he is discrete.

Chapter Seventeen
The friendship between Gallia and Margaret develops quickly. On a walk in Grosvenor Park, they are joined by Margaret's friend, Gertrude Janion. The three women are observed by Essex and Gurdon.

Chapter Eighteen
Gallia, Margaret and Gertrude compare their views on men and love. Margaret and Gertrude are not persuaded that Gallia's eugenicist ideas would ever be acceptable to most men and women and Gertrude suspects her of having been jilted.

Chapter Nineteen
Lord Hamesthwaite is planning a house party for political colleagues at his country home, and encourages Gallia to invite

Margaret and Mrs Essex for her own company. Gallia visits her aunt, and asks her to join them in the country after her trip to France. Mark Gurdon's name has just been raised when he is announced. Lord Hamesthwaite is coming to dinner. Mrs Leighton asks Gallia and Gurdon to join them, and to go on to Holland House in the evening. Gallia drives to the House of Lords, to tell her father of the arrangements. While she is waiting for him in the cloisters of Westminster Abbey, she is discovered by Dark Essex.

Chapter Twenty
Seeing Essex, Gallia recognises that, though she will never love another man, the life she wishes to lead cannot possibly include him. She is, he tells her, 'simply incapable of ordinary feminine feeling... a misshapen woman'. When she describes her passionate desire to mother a child, he finds himself oddly drawn to her. He kisses her with passion. Essex is being sincere, 'for the first time in his life perhaps'.

Chapter Twenty-One
That night, Essex walks home to Hammersmith thinking of Gallia: the confused and puzzlingly pleasurable memory of the courtyard scene stays with him. Essex's kiss has given Gallia a fullness of beauty she has never possessed before, and Gurdon is captivated. Returning home, Gurdon discovers that Cara is dangerously ill. She has induced a miscarriage by dancing. A doctor is called.

Chapter Twenty-Two
Two weeks later, Gallia is overseeing the preparations for leaving London, when a charlady falls from a ladder and is badly injured. Gallia tends her while a doctor is sought. The charlady, Mrs Miles, is anxious that a letter entrusted to her by 'Missie', a sick young woman in her care, should be posted without delay. Gallia offers to help, and is handed a letter addressed to Mark Gurdon, in Gurdon's own handwriting.

Chapter Twenty-Three

Gallia and her father travel down to their Surrey residence. In the interim, Mrs Miles has confided more information about Gurdon and his mistress, not knowing that Gallia and Gurdon are acquainted. Gallia decides that her initial moral revulsion is unjustified. Stopping at a village inn she sees Essex stretched out asleep in a chair. She leaves, taking care not to let him see her.

Chapter Twenty-Four

Margaret has now arrived to stay with the Hamesthwaites. She and Gallia talk about men (Essex in particular), and Gallia raises the subject of mistresses. Letters arrive announcing the imminent arrival of Mr Denyer – a key figure in Britain's handling of a recent (unspecified) crisis in Britain's relations with South Africa. Robbie Leighton is also expected. Margaret is tellingly pensive when she hears he is coming.

Chapter Twenty-Five

After a meeting in London with Mr Denyer, Lord Hamesthwaite unexpectedly asks his daughter to include Mark Gurdon on the list of invitations to the house party. Gurdon has made himself discretely indispensable to the Colonial Office on his recent trip to Central Africa. His arrival is followed by that of Robbie. Margaret's greeting and Robbie's response leave Gallia and Gurdon in no doubt that the two are in love. Gallia's stately greeting of Mr Denyer confirms Gurdon in his admiration of her. Essex joins the party.

Chapter Twenty-Six

Miss Janion has now joined the party, and Gallia decides on a day trip to Hindhead. Essex joins the group, and his thoughts are of the emotions which led him to kiss Gallia. Gurdon's thoughts are occupied with Cara, now recuperating in Brighton; his satisfaction with his own handling of the African business; and his feeling that he is now well on his way to a distinguished future.

Chapter Twenty-Seven

Margaret and Robbie take a romantic walk. Essex contrives a private interview with Gallia. Alone, they talk at length about how intensely she once loved him, and how cruelly he treated her. When she states that Gurdon possesses all the virile qualities she desires (and which Essex clearly lacks) Essex agrees. His approval leaves her a little discontented. He tells her that the moment she stopped loving him was the moment he started loving her. They part decorously.

Chapter Twenty-Eight

Gurdon and Gallia are on their way home when the horse stumbles and becomes lame. They stop at an inn, and make arrangements to return by train. In the meantime the conversation quickly becomes intimate, and Mark tells her that he wants her to be his wife. She tells him that she had decided to marry him before he raised the question. Mark is overjoyed, but Gallia gives voice to her dismay at the sentimental appeal the situation makes to her, in spite of all her nobler intentions. At her bidding, Mark picks meadowsweet and honeysuckle and drapes them over her.

Chapter Twenty-Nine

Gallia asks Mark if he likes children, and he replies that he would love *their* children. She is suddenly overwhelmed with the wish that Essex, not Mark, were beside her. When Mark asks her to tell him that she loves him, she informs him that she is marrying him because she wants him to be the father of her children. He confesses that he once loved Margaret Essex, and she is unconcerned, but takes the opportunity to tell him that she is also fully aware that he has kept a mistress. Mark is dumbfounded by her lack of feminine jealousy, and appalled to realize that she genuinely has no love for him. As they walk from the station to the Hamesthwaites' home, he slowly recovers from the shock, and determines that he will teach her to love him. When she gravely asserts that she will be disappointed in herself if he succeeds, he has the manly 'grit' to laugh and take her in his arms.

Chapter Thirty

Back at the house, Mrs Leighton has arrived. Gallia retires to bed early. In the morning she tells her father that she wishes to marry Gurdon, and receives his approval. Margaret and Robbie are also engaged. Essex reveals that he has heart disease and Gurdon takes him into the smoking-room for a private interview. When Essex re-emerges, Gallia notes his curious pallor and questions him. He tells her that his heart was irreparably damaged in his rowing days and that the weakness is hereditary. She listens with a 'curious light in her eyes'. They promise to meet again, after her marriage. For now, Essex has to fulfil a promise to Mark Gurdon by going to Brighton and telling Cara Lemuel that her lover is to be married.

ACKNOWLEDGEMENTS

I am grateful to Sir Mark Norman for his generosity in answering questions about Ménie Muriel Dowie's life, and for allowing me access to family letters and photographs. Lady Norman, Torquil Norman and Alexander Norman have also assisted me by sharing personal reminiscences. Patrick French kindly allowed me to check details of Ménie Muriel Dowie's life against his research into the life of Sir Henry Norman, and alerted me to material I should otherwise have missed.

For advice on matters of annotation, I am indebted to John Kerrigan, Malcolm Schofield, Alastair Small and Sheila Stern.

WOMEN'S WRITING
IN EVERYMAN

A SELECTION

Female Playwrights of the Restoration
FIVE COMEDIES
Rediscovered literary treasures in a unique selection **£5.99**

The Secret Self
SHORT STORIES BY WOMEN
'A superb collection' *Guardian* **£4.99**

Short Stories
KATHERINE MANSFIELD
An excellent selection displaying the remarkable range of Mansfield's talent **£3.99**

Women Romantic Poets 1780-1830: An Anthology
Hidden talent from the Romantic era rediscovered **£5.99**

Selected Poems
ELIZABETH BARRETT
BROWNING
A major contribution to our appreciation of this inspiring and innovative poet **£5.99**

Frankenstein
MARY SHELLEY
A masterpiece of Gothic terror in its original 1818 version **£3.99**

The Life of Charlotte Brontë
ELIZABETH GASKELL
A moving and perceptive tribute by one writer to another **£4.99**

Vindication of the Rights of Woman and The Subjection of Women
MARY WOLLSTONECRAFT
AND J. S. MILL
Two pioneering works of early feminist thought **£4.99**

The Pastor's Wife
ELIZABETH VON ARNIM
A funny and accomplished novel by the author of *Elizabeth and Her German Garden* **£5.99**

EVERYMAN

BELINDA

MARIA EDGEWORTH

£6.99

AVAILABILITY
All books are available from your local bookshop or direct from
**Littlehampton Book Services Cash Sales, 14 Eldon Way, Lineside Estate,
Littlehampton, West Sussex BN17 7HE.** PRICES ARE SUBJECT TO CHANGE.

To order any of the books, please enclose a cheque (in £ sterling) made payable to Littlehampton Book Services, or phone your order through with credit card details (Access, Visa or Mastercard) on 0903 721596 (24 hour answering service) stating card number and expiry date. Please add £1.25 for package and postage to the total value of your order.

In the USA, for further information and a complete catalogue call 1-800-526-2778.

SHORT STORY COLLECTIONS
IN EVERYMAN

A SELECTION

The Secret Self 1: Short Stories by Women
'A superb collection' *Guardian* **£4.99**

Selected Short Stories and Poems
THOMAS HARDY
The best of Hardy's Wessex in a unique selection **£4.99**

The Best of Sherlock Holmes
ARTHUR CONAN DOYLE
All the favourite adventures in one volume **£4.99**

Great Tales of Detection Nineteen Stories
Chosen by Dorothy L. Sayers **£3.99**

Short Stories
KATHERINE MANSFIELD
A selection displaying the remarkable range of Mansfield's writing **£3.99**

Selected Stories
RUDYARD KIPLING
Includes stories chosen to reveal the 'other' Kipling **£4.50**

The Strange Case of Dr Jekyll and Mr Hyde and Other Stories
R. L. STEVENSON
An exciting selection of gripping tales from a master of suspense **£3.99**

The Day of Silence and Other Stories
GEORGE GISSING
Gissing's finest stories, available for the first time in one volume **£4.99**

Selected Tales
HENRY JAMES
Stories portraying the tensions between private life and the outside world **£5.99**

£4.99

AVAILABILITY
All books are available from your local bookshop or direct from
Littlehampton Book Services Cash Sales, 14 Eldon Way, Lineside Estate, Littlehampton, West Sussex BN17 7HE. PRICES ARE SUBJECT TO CHANGE.

To order any of the books, please enclose a cheque (in £ sterling) made payable to Littlehampton Book Services, or phone your order through with credit card details (Access, Visa or Mastercard) on 0903 721596 (24 hour answering service) stating card number and expiry date. Please add £1.25 for package and postage to the total value of your order.

In the USA, for further information and a complete catalogue call 1-800-526-2778.

CLASSIC FICTION
IN EVERYMAN

A SELECTION

Frankenstein
MARY SHELLEY
A masterpiece of Gothic terror in its
original 1818 version **£3.99**

Dracula
BRAM STOKER
One of the best known horror stories
in the world **£3.99**

The Diary of A Nobody
GEORGE AND WEEDON
GROSSMITH
A hilarious account of suburban life
in Edwardian London **£4.99**

Some Experiences
and Further Experiences
of an Irish R. M.
SOMERVILLE AND ROSS
Gems of comic exuberance and
improvisation **£4.50**

Three Men in a Boat
JEROME K. JEROME
English humour at its best **£2.99**

Twenty Thousand Leagues
under the Sea
JULES VERNE
Scientific fact combines with
fantasy in this prophetic tale of
underwater adventure **£4.99**

The Best of Father Brown
G. K. CHESTERTON
An irresistible selection of crime
stories – unique to Everyman **£4.99**

The Collected Raffles
E. W. HORNUNG
Dashing exploits from the most glam-
orous figure in crime fiction **£4.99**

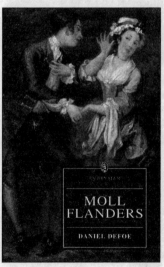

£5.99

AVAILABILITY

All books are available from your local bookshop or direct from
**Littlehampton Book Services Cash Sales, 14 Eldon Way, Lineside Estate,
Littlehampton, West Sussex BN17 7HE.** PRICES ARE SUBJECT TO CHANGE.

To order any of the books, please enclose a cheque (in £ sterling) made payable to
Littlehampton Book Services, or phone your order through with credit card details (Access,
Visa or Mastercard) on 0903 721596 (24 hour answering service) stating card number and
expiry date. Please add £1.25 for package and postage to the total value of your order.

In the USA, for further information and a complete catalogue call 1-800-526-2778.

AMERICAN LITERATURE IN EVERYMAN

A SELECTION

Selected Poems
HENRY LONGFELLOW
A new selection spanning the whole of Longfellow's literary career **£7.99**

Typee
HERMAN MELVILLE
Melville's stirring debut, drawing directly on his own adventures in the South Seas **£4.99**

Billy Budd and Other Stories
HERMAN MELVILLE
The compelling parable of innocence destroyed by a fallen world **£4.99**

The Last of the Mohicans
JAMES FENIMORE COOPER
The classic tale of old America, full of romantic adventure **£5.99**

The Scarlet Letter
NATHANIEL HAWTHORNE
The compelling tale of an independent woman's struggle against a crushing moral code **£3.99**

The Red Badge of Courage
STEPHEN CRANE
A vivid portrayal of a young soldier's experience of the American Civil War **£2.99**

Essays and Poems
RALPH WALDO EMERSON
An indispensable edition celebrating one of the most influential American writers **£5.99**

The Federalist
HAMILTON, MADISON AND JAY
Classics of political science, these essays helped to found the American Constitution **£6.99**

Leaves of Grass and Selected Prose
WALT WHITMAN
The best of Whitman in one volume **£6.99**

£5.99

AVAILABILITY

All books are available from your local bookshop or direct from
Littlehampton Book Services Cash Sales, 14 Eldon Way, Lineside Estate, Littlehampton, West Sussex BN17 7HE. PRICES ARE SUBJECT TO CHANGE.

To order any of the books, please enclose a cheque (in £ sterling) made payable to Littlehampton Book Services, or phone your order through with credit card details (Access, Visa or Mastercard) on 0903 721596 (24 hour answering service) stating card number and expiry date. Please add £1.25 for package and postage to the total value of your order.

In the USA, for further information and a complete catalogue call 1-800-526-2778.